Mathematical Encounters of the Second Kind

For Gail Corbett

Philip J. Davis

Mathematical Encounters of the Second Kind

BIRKHÄUSER

Boston • Basel • Berlin

Philip J. Davis
Division of Applied Mathematics
Brown University
Providence, RI 02912

Library of Congress Cataloging-in-Publication Data

Davis, Philip J., 1923-
    Mathematical encounters of the second kind / Philip J. Davis.
        p.   cm.
    ISBN 0-8176-3939-X (hardcover : alk. paper). -- ISBN 3-7643-3939-X
(hardcover : alk. paper)
      1. Mathematics.   2. Mathematicians.   I. Title.
    QA10.5.D38   1996
    510--dc20   96-22131
                            CIP

Printed on acid-free paper

© 1997 Birkhäuser Boston   *Birkhäuser* ®

ISBN 0-8176-3939-X
ISBN 3-7643-3939-X
Designed and typeset by Martin Stock, Cambridge, MA
Cover design by Joseph Sherman, Dutton and Sherman Design, Hamden, CT
Original drawing (Carpenter p. 56) by Marguerite Dorian, Providence, RI
Printed and bound by Hamilton Printing, Rensselaer, NY
Printed in the U.S.A.

9 8 7 6 5 4 3 2 1

CONTENTS

PREFACE

A number of years ago, Harriet Sheridan, then Dean of Brown University, organized a series of lectures in which individual faculty members described how it came about that they entered their various fields. I was invited to participate in this series and found in the invitation an opportunity to recall events going back to my early teens. The lecture was well received and its reception encouraged me to work up an expanded version. My manuscript lay dormant all these years. In the meanwhile, sufficiently many other mathematical experiences and encounters accumulated to make this little book. My 1981 lecture is the basis of the first piece: "Napoleon's Theorem."

Although there is a connection between the first piece and the second, the four pieces here are essentially independent. The second piece, "Carpenter and the Napoleon Ascription," has as its object a full description of a certain type of scholar-storyteller (of whom I have known and admired several). It is a pastiche, containing a salad bar selection blended together by my own imagination. This piece purports, as a secondary goal, to present a solution to a certain unsolved historical problem raised in the first piece.

The third piece, "The Man Who Began His Lectures with 'Namely'," is a short reminiscence of Stefan Bergman, one of my teachers of graduate mathematics. Bergman, a remarkable personality, was born in Poland and came to the United States in 1939.

With several notable exceptions, serious and sustained mathematical research in the United States did not begin until the 1880's. Since that time, native-born researchers have been joined and stimulated by a constant stream of highly trained and talented mathematicians from abroad. The disastrous world events of 1935–1946 increased the flow greatly. The emigration of European scientists led, in the post–WWII years, to the preeminence of the United States in mathematical matters. Bergman was part of that stream and I intend this profile to serve also as a tribute to the many other exiles of this period from whom I have learned so much.

The fourth and last piece, "The Rothschild I Knew," is different again. It tells how a casual mathematical inquiry from Lord Victor Rothschild (of England), himself a distinguished biochemist, grew into a substantial friendship, and allowed me glimpses of worlds to which I would otherwise have had no access.

Since I myself am fond of listening to and telling stories, I have not limited myself to minimalist presentations. I have been called a "tangentialist" by a Polish (!) critic, and I wear that designation with considerable pride. The patient reader will find that there are many stories here that have little or nothing to do with mathematics as such.

With regard to the title, I call involvement with mathematics itself "encounters of the first kind." I reserve the term "encounters of the second kind" for mathematical involvement with people or with tangential questions such as have been developed in this book. Inevitably, there are a number of places in this book where mathematics appears. The reader who cannot handle such material can skip over it lightly without loss of the purely human themes.

Mathematics is one of the greatest intellectual creations of the human mind. It is a language, a method, an attitude, a world both of arcane formulas, and of the strange and wonderful ideas that underlie them. It is a craft, an art, a science. It has given birth to philosophy, to computer systems, and has unlocked certain aspects of the universe. It has also given birth to stories about people. I hope the stories presented here add to the already distinguished corpus of encounters of the second kind.

P.J. Davis

I

Napoleon's Theorem

Quod vitæ sectabor iter?

What path shall I take through life?

— Ausonius (310–393)
Dreamed by René Descartes
November 10, 1619

P.J. Davis, age 14, works on Napoleon's Theorem. His father looks on and wonders what it's all about.

1
Phillips and Fisher

I begin with kerosene at seven cents a gallon. In Northeastern Massachusetts this was its price in the winter of 1936. The winter was fierce and the economic depression was worse. My father could not afford to heat more than one room of our house – the kitchen, naturally. And so we lived in the kitchen, as did many of our neighbors. There was my father, my mother, and I; my older brothers and sister were away. When it was time for bed, I opened the door of an icy bedroom, closed it behind me carefully, and lay down between two quilts on top and an old khaki army blanket underneath.

The kitchen remained warm, too warm perhaps. It was heated by a large black Glenwood coal stove which had belonged to my grandfather and which my father had converted to kerosene. I had the job of hauling kerosene a pail at a time from a storage tank in the cellar.

On weekdays I got home from high school around two in the afternoon. I fetched a pail of oil up the stairs, and turned up both burners to number 4 or 5. Ten minutes later the wicks "burnt in" and the coils glowed. I opened the oven door and a copious supply of heat poured out. I pulled up a rocking chair to the stove and placed a drawing board across its arms and settled down to do my homework.

This regime lasted for five winters, from 1933 to 1938. Do I romanticize? It did not seem romantic at the time. It was what it was, and I didn't think about it too much. I saw my father's difficulties clearly, how he had come down in the world. Despite this I felt well off, for I had classmates who had less even than I; and grown-ups talked in hush-hush tones about this man and that man who had committed suicide under economic stress. I worried much more for my father's future than for my own. I was on a path through life, and though I could not identify what path it was, its traces were as clear to me as those of the Indian trail that followed the Merrimack River.

In my sophomore year at high school I took Algebra 2, Geometry, French, Latin, and English. The geometry caught me as it catches many young people. Our class studied from an updated and watered-down version of Euclid. In imitation of Euclid's original *Elements*, our text was divided into "books." Book I dealt with triangles, congruence, and parallels, Book II with circles, arcs, chords, Book III with proportion, Book IV with areas, and so on. In these books I found a new world and a new method for dealing with it. In geometry I met the essence of mathematics, its pure forms and abstractions, far removed from life and death, from economics and politics. I found logical deduction, and naked reason exposed; I found certainty beyond controversy. Or so I thought at the time. Here also in geometry was an arena for individual skill, for ingenuity and intuition all pitted against the inherent difficulties of geometrical nature and the stubbornness of mathematical fact. Here, in a word, I found a form of intoxication.

In the beginning, geometry posed no difficulties and held no terrors for me. I read that King Ptolemy once asked Euclid whether there was a shorter way of achieving a knowledge of geometry than by reading the *Elements*. Euclid answered that there was no royal road to geometry. I thought this irrelevant as far as I was concerned, for I zipped through the textbook well ahead of the daily assignments and did all the problems (they were called "originals" in my school). I became an expert at handling the ruler and compass and made constructions and models of all sorts.

In geometry I discovered the thrill of the chase and saw the unfolding and interlocking of mathematical ideas. I experienced how the tension of what is unknown and unresolved gradually yields to catharsis when solutions are reached. In geometry I also found a link between the real world of vision and movement, of extent and shape, of line and curve and surface, and the imaginary and symbolic world of their mathematical counterparts. The connection was so vivid, so right, that I did not wonder (as I would years later) how it is possible in the nature of things to make a marriage between the real and the symbolic. I mastered the symbolic world, and it seemed to compel the physical world to behave.

I sat for hours before the open stove. When the weather grew warmer I moved to the "den" in the back of the house. With ruler and compass and stacks of paper, I played geometrical variations and fugues. In retrospect I doubt if I ever again was able to concentrate to such an extent. The months flew by and my skill increased. Early on, I made the transition from reading and duplicating to making things up for myself. My grandest achievement in high school was to pose and solve a problem which years later I found had been posed and solved by Apollonius of Perga in 200 BC: Given three circles, how can one determine a fourth circle which shall be tangent to the three, with the aid of only a ruler and compass and confining oneself to the classic rules of operating with these instruments?

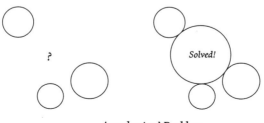

Appolonius' Problem

It is a well-known fact, I parallel the epigram of Jane Austen, that a young student who is good at one subject is very likely to be good at other subjects. So it was in my case.

What, then, narrowed the field to mathematics? Why not enter law, medicine, business, or engineering? Why not tinker, tailor, soldier, sailor? Why select a field where the demands of success are severe and whose employment opportunities in those days were practically non-existent?

I blame it on two Yale professors, whom I never knew. I owned a geometry book by Phillips and Fisher, a book that was older (it was published in 1897) and harder than the one we used in school. The book belonged to one of my brothers – I forget which one. In the back of the book there was a supplemental collection of problems. I worked through these problems as a beaver gnaws through the trunk of a tree. Ultimately, I came to Problem 43. A surprising thing happened: I got stuck. I couldn't do it. I spent hours on it and nothing worked. I tried this and that and everything failed. All my ingenious construction lines, those magic catalysts of Euclid and twenty later generations of geometers, came to nought.

Ultimately, I moved on to Problem 44. It seemed to be related to Problem 43. I couldn't do this one either. After some weeks I had made slight progress. I learned how, if I could solve Problem 43, I could solve Problem 44 and vice versa. That was nice, that was interesting, but it was cold comfort, for I could solve neither of them. (Years later, I would learn that many unsolved problems in mathematics are related in pairs or in groups of equivalent problems, all of which defy proof.)

I skipped that pair of problems for the time being and worked out the others. What was particularly infuriating about my failure was that Phillips and Fisher had placed the problem within the context of Book II material. This meant that it could not have been

EXERCISES 467

41. If two points are given on the circumference of a given circle, another fixed circle can be found such that if any two lines be drawn from the given points to intersect on its circumference, the straight line joining the points in which these lines meet the given circle a second time will be of constant length.

42. If the three diagonals joining the opposite vertices of a hexagon are equal and the opposite sides are parallel in pairs, the hexagon can be inscribed in a circle.

43. Equilateral triangles are constructed on the sides of a given triangle and external to it. Prove that the three lines, each joining the outer vertex of one of the equilateral triangles to the opposite vertex of the given triangle, meet in a point and are equal.

44. On each side of a triangle construct an isosceles triangle with the adjacent angles equal to 30°. Prove that the straight lines joining the outer vertices of these three triangles are equal.

LOCI

45. One side and the opposite angle of a triangle are given, and equilateral triangles are constructed on the other two (variable) sides. Find the locus of the middle point of the straight line joining the outer vertices of the equilateral triangles.

46. Through a vertex of an equilateral triangle is drawn any straight line *PQ*, terminated by the perpendiculars to the opposite side erected at the extremities of that side; on *PQ* as a side a second equilateral triangle is constructed. Find the locus of the opposite vertex of the second equilateral triangle.

47. The sides of a right triangle are given in position, its hypotenuse in length. Find the locus of the middle point of the hypotenuse.

48. *AC, BD,* are fixed diameters of a circle, at right angles to each other, and *P* is any point on the circumference. *PA* cuts *BD* in *E*; *EF*, parallel to *AC*, cuts *PB* in *F*. Prove that the locus of *F* is a straight line.

The source of my difficulty: Problems 43 and 44 of Elements of Geometry, *Phillips and Fisher, 1897.*

too difficult. I had done much, much harder things. When I entered college, I had not yet solved the problem. There is no royal road to geometry.

Let's take a look at Problem 44. What it says is this (I'm going to modify the statement very slightly):

Draw a triangle; no special triangular shape is required. On each of its sides, construct outwardly equilateral triangles. (Recall that an equilateral triangle is one in which the sides have equal lengths and the angles are all 60°.) Now mark the centers of the equilateral triangles. Finally, connect the three centers with straight line segments, and these segments will themselves form an equilateral triangle.

This is a lovely theorem and many things coalesce to make it so. The figure is built from the simplest materials: a few straight line segments. The equilateral triangles are most easily put in place with a few swings of a compass so that the figure can be drafted in a minute or so. If one draws the figure carefully, one can submit the statement to experimental verification: simply measure the dotted line segments and see whether they are equal.

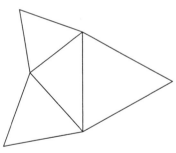

A triangle with
three equilateral triangles
constructed outwardly
on its sides.

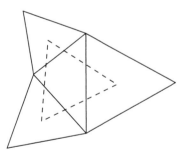

The centers of the equilateral
triangles themselves are vertices
of an equilateral triangle.

There is still another reason why the theorem is nice. One starts from a random triangle and does certain things to it. The same kind of thing is done on each side. Then, lo and behold, what emerges is *not* random at all. It is an equilateral triangle and consequently a highly structured figure. This is a great surprise, and a very simple example of how order can emerge from chaos. Here is the Genesis story exhibited mathematically with a ruler and compass construction.

I realized all this as a schoolboy. The aesthetics didn't help me arrive at a solution, but they elevated the problem to one of high distinction and kept me slugging away at it. Charmed by geometry at the age of twelve, I was hooked by thirteen by a problem I could not solve, a problem set by two Yale professors.

In later years I used to think about these men and where they got Problem 44. The senior partner of the writing team, Andrew Phillips, had been a Connecticut farm boy born in Jewett City in 1844. He went neither to secondary school nor to college. Something about mathematics grabbed him, and with the aid of a tutor he studied the subject, rising professionally and becoming professor at Yale in the 1870's. Don't think that his mother didn't worry about him: how could he make a living from this mathematical and professorial tomfoolery? His boyhood friends were already doing so well in business. Ah, those Yankee mothers.

Phillips

Phillips does not tell us what precisely intrigued him about mathematics, but his interest occurred early. He wrote: "How many times have I let the oxen rest under the shade of a big tree as I smoothed off the rough ground and drew geometrical diagrams while the oxen looked at me with tender eyes and chewed their cuds with contentment and happiness."

Phillips was a fine teacher, an excellent maker of mathematical models and the author of a number of books on elementary mathematics. A faithful churchgoer, he combined Yankee piety with an interest in spiritualism. In his day, spiritualism was the vice of intellectual New England and was academicized when the great William James set up an institute at Harvard for the study of parapsychic phenomena.

Fisher

The younger partner, and as it turned out, the much more distinguished partner scientifically, was Irving Fisher. Fisher started his career in mathematics, but later shifted over to economics. His Yale Ph.D. thesis of 1891 was on the theory of value and prices. The mathematics never left him and Fisher became one of the founders of the subject of mathematical economics or econometrics as it is sometimes called. Probably the greatest economist the U.S. has yet produced, Fisher was a mild eccentric, a pamphleteer for health causes, an extraordinarily clear and convincing expositor with words, with graphs, and with mathematics. In the late twenties Fisher took the plunge, failed to anticipate the crash, and lost his shirt. Don't think the public didn't cry: physician heal thyself.

I like to think that Problem 44, my nemesis, was proposed by Fisher. I like to imagine that Phillips who, as I have said, was the older man and Fisher's teacher (he was also the teacher of the great physicist Josiah Willard Gibbs), probably said to his younger colleague, "Fisher, we've got to have a bunch of good problems for our book on geometry. Keep the young bloods on their toes. Go out and collect a few." And Fisher scrounged around for problems in other textbooks and in mathematical journals devoted to secondary education. He might even have made up his own.

Some way, somehow, Problem 44 found its way into their book, and from there into my consciousness. I will not go so far as to say that if I had knocked off Problem 44 at the age of thirteen, my mathematical career would have ended then and there in a blaze of self-satisfaction. No, the fascination with mathematics was already substantial. The problem played its part and it was a significant one. It stood on my horizon unsolved, a puzzle, a challenge, a reproach, a spur, a duty to be discharged, an intensifier: I wanted to learn enough mathematics to put the quietus on it once and for all.

In my junior year in high school I took Algebra 3, and in my senior year trigonometry and solid geometry. I studied calculus on my own. I avoided Problem 44. Defeated, I retreated, licked my wounds and husbanded my strength. I monitored the enemy out of the corner of my eye. At some point in the future when I was more experienced, when I was in possession of more formidable weapons, I would sally forth and do battle.

2

Descartes

The modern world, a world of triumphant rationality (if you can believe that), began on November 10, 1619 with a revelation and a nightmare. On that day, in a room in the small Bavarian village of Ulm, René Descartes, a twenty-three year old Frenchman, crawled into a wall stove and, when he was well warmed, had a vision. It was not a vision of God or of the Mother of God or of celestial chariots or of the New Jerusalem: it was a vision of the unification of all science.

The vision was preceded by a state of intense concentration and agitation. Descartes' overheated mind caught fire and provided answers to the tremendous problems that had been taxing him for weeks. He was possessed by a Genius, and the answers were revealed in a dazzling and unendurable light. Later, in a state of exhaustion, he went to bed and dreamed three dreams that had been predicted by this Genius.

René Descartes
1596–1650

In the first dream he was revolved by a whirlwind and terrified by phantoms. He experienced a constant feeling of falling. He imagined he would be presented with a melon that came from a far-off land. The wind abated and he woke up. His second dream was one of thunderclaps and sparks flying around his room. In the third dream, all was quiet and contemplative. An anthology of poetry lay on the table. He opened it at random and read the verse *"Quod vitæ sectabor iter."* A stranger appeared and quoted him the verse *"Est et Non"* (Yes and No). Descartes wanted to show him where in the anthology it could be found, but the book disappeared and reappeared. He told the man he would show him a better verse beginning "Quod vitae sectabor iter." At this point, the man, the book, and the whole dream dissolved.

Descartes was so bewildered by all this that he began to pray. He assumed his dreams had a supernatural origin. He vowed he would put his life under the protection of the Blessed Virgin and go on a pilgrimage from Venice to Notre Dame de Lorette, traveling by foot and wearing the humblest clothes he could find.

Eighteen years passed before the world would have the details of the grandiose vision and of the *"mirabilis scientiæ fundamenta"* – the foundations of a marvellous science. Such as he was able to give them, they are contained in his celebrated *Discourse on the Method of Properly Guiding Reason in the Search for Truth in the Sciences.* Method thinking, according to Descartes, should be applied when knowledge is sought in any scientific field. It consists of (a) accepting only what is so clear in one's own mind as to exclude any doubt, (b) splitting large difficulties into smaller ones, (c) arguing from the simple to the complex, and (d) checking after one is done.

Descartes was first and foremost a geometer and claimed he was in the habit of turning all things into geometry. What would give the method substance, what would form a universal basis, was the use of mathematics, the science of space and quantity, which was the simplest and the surest of the conceptions of the mind. Cartesianism calls for the primacy of world mathematization.

★　★　★

When I was in high school and first heard about analytic geometry, also called coordinate geometry or Cartesian geometry, I thought that it derived entirely from Descartes and that it offered a powerful way of reducing all problems in geometry to a corresponding problem in algebra. The problem in algebra could then be solved in a simple and automatic way. The ingenuity required in the classical geometry of Euclid would be eliminated and replaced by a definite procedure. These views must have been in the air and I simply picked them up. One even heard it said that analytic geometry was like a huge meat grinder: one stuffed the problem in, turned the crank, and out came the answer.

13

The truth is not so simple. Anyone familiar with analytic geometry as it is taught today will not recognize it in Descartes' revolutionary book. What one finds there is not so much coordinate geometry as the algebraization of ruler and compass constructions. Coordinate geometry as currently taught involves the placing of perpendicular axes in a plane, the assignment of two coordinates (or addresses) to each geometrical point, and the replacement of straight lines and curves by appropriate algebraic equations. In its current form, Cartesian geometry is due as much to Descartes' own contemporaries and successors as to himself.

It is true that in a logical sense, analytic geometry is a machine for deciding the truth of geometric statements in an automatic way. This was established by the logician Alfred Tarski, but not until 1931, and in a format which is not applicable to geometric questions that came up in practice. Usually, when one works analytically, ingenuity is required in setting up the algebra and in handling its details. Without this ingenuity, the algebra itself can become so formidable as to vitiate the presumed automatic quality of the method.

Nonetheless, for the fierceness and the universality of his vision, for his philosophy which stressed the role of the thinking individual, if not for the precise details of world mathematization, it is correct to call Descartes the first modern man and to call ourselves Cartesians.

What was bugging Descartes? Or as Paul Valéry, the French poet and essayist who studied Descartes over a lifetime wrote in his notebooks, "Find what Descartes wanted. What it was possible for him to want, what he coveted, if only half consciously. There's the base, the strategic point to be clarified."

Some scholars think that Descartes had been playing around with Rosicrucian doctrine. Many scientists of the period were members of this brotherhood or had studied its precepts. These scholars think that Descartes wanted to raise the hermetic and alchemic universalism of Rosicrucians to the level of precise reason that he found in mathematical deduction. More generally, it is thought that Descartes found that the current state of knowledge was an uncritical mixture of fact and fancy, of legend and hearsay, of sense and nonsense, of doctrine and dogma, of experiment and traditional authority, of conjecture and prejudice, all infused with stale and ineffective metaphysics and with chaotic and misguided procedures. All this he wanted to reform and revolutionize, to sweep away and replace by a method which was sure and truth-revealing. He wanted to underwrite the new science with a new vision of truth and a new philosophy. To this grandiose program he dedicated his life, saying, "I have put it above kingdoms and thrones and held riches as naught compared to it."

Without denying the reformist motivation, I should like to suggest that there was another element that lent its strength to Descartes' program. I like to imagine that as a young boy he was confronted with a certain problem in mathematics. He tried this and that in order to solve it, and nothing worked. He got stuck. He simply could not solve the problem.

There is nothing peculiar about this supposition. All mathematicians get stuck. The very greatest of mathematical geniuses get stuck. And the proof of this statement is evident: there are always famous unsolved problems around. That some of these problems ultimately get solved is irrelevant. In every generation, there is something that the best brains can't do.

Mathematics, said Descartes, is a thing of the mind. Its truths, proceeding as they do from sure hypotheses through tiny but equally sure steps of human reason, are guaranteed by God. Why should the mind block itself? If it conceives of a problem it must equally reveal the path along which the solution is to be found.

I like to imagine that, having been stuck, a kind of cosmic fury lasting a lifetime arose in the young Descartes, which he sought to dissipate by finding a method guaranteed to produce answers.

Early in 1940, having taken a fine course in Descartes' geometry, or rather, in coordinate geometry as it had subsequently developed in the hands of the masters of the craft, I turned my attention to Problem 44. I expected that I would insert the problem into Descartes' machine, turn the crank, and routinely, automatically, this rational machine would deliver the solution to me.

I tried. I failed. The crank would not crank, the grinder would not grind. There is no royal road to geometry.

3
Napoleon

I received my B.S. in mathematics in 1943. Shortly thereafter, I taught college mathematics for the first time. From 1944 to 1946, as a member of the United States Air Force Reserve, I was employed as a mathematician and physicist at NACA (The National Advisory Committee for Aeronautics; now NASA) at Langley Field, Virginia. In 1950 I received my Ph.D. in mathematics from Harvard and entered into post-doctoral research. My interests and attitudes were now wholly professional. As the years rolled on, Problem 44 receded into the background, along with the Minuet in G that I once played on the piano and other such juvenilia. If I thought about the problem at all, my thoughts were Parnassian, viewing the matter from the top of a mountain of knowledge and experience.

The theorem struck me still as a pretty one, but inconsequential, of no practical use to anyone. Consider the lilies of the field; they toil not, neither do they spin. Well, Problem 44 was a mathematical lily. It was not the key to the atoms or the galaxies or biological processes, nor was it the key to the business cycles. Nonetheless, it was somehow inextricably connected with how the universe is put together. Granted our geometrical perceptions, granted our rules of logical inference, then Problem 44 follows as the night follows the day.

I could prove it any time I wanted. After all, it was just an exercise in a high school textbook. It could have been thought up by the ancient Greek mathematicians. It might have been mentioned by Euclid or Pappus, that busy collector of problems five centuries later. It might have been; but as far as I know, it was not.

Realizing all this, I never bothered to work out a proof of my own. From time to time I saw the problem mentioned in the geometrical literature. I ignored it. Occasionally, a proof was appended, and there are proofs that can be given in four or five lines, proofs that I certainly would have understood at the age of thirteen, but I was indifferent to them. I even formulated a theory of why, as a boy, I had not been able to solve the problem. It had to do with the fact that I was looking for a proof using purely geometric or visual means and not algebraic ones. I wanted to append to the figure a few lines, so ingeniously placed that the whole matter would be exposed to the naked eye. I wanted to be able to say not ὅπερ ἔδει δεῖξαι (*quod erat demonstrandum*), as did the ancient Greek mathematicians, but simply, "Lo and behold! The matter is as plain as the nose on your face." This kind of simplicity and elegance has high appeal and ultimately great transparency, but its discovery may come harder.

In 1961 I was browsing in a scientific bookstore in Cambridge,

Massachusetts, where I happened to take a look at the newly published *Introduction to Geometry* by H.S.M. Coxeter. I knew the author was a very distinguished mathematician at the University of Toronto. Flipping through Coxeter's book quite at random, I found, on pages 22–23, my old Problems 43 and 44, together with sophisticated proofs. Now this raised my eyebrows, for Coxeter obviously thought that my Old Nemesis was sufficiently interesting to devote a half page to it. What also caught my eye was a footnote to the effect that the theorem was attributed to Napoleon. Napoleon? Napoleon I? Napoleon III? No, surely not the latter. Napoleon Bonaparte it had to be; the Little Corporal. Did Charlemagne or Louis XIV have a theorem ascribed to them? No. Did Alexander of Macedeon or King Ptolemy I? No. But old Boney did. Was this ascription reasonable? Though Coxeter expressed some doubts, I thought it was reasonable; that is to say, I thought it was not unreasonable, which is a somewhat different thing.

The young Napoleon was good at mathematics. In fact, one can still read the report of his academy examiners and learn that he was good at mathematics and not so hot in other subjects.

Problem 44 was just the kind of thing that might be discovered by any young devotee fooling around with ruler and compass. Having convinced himself of the truth, he announced the fact. He may or may not have proved it in the strict sense. This is irrelevant, for truth and proof are separate things.

It is also known that Napoleon, in command of France, liked to surround himself with scientists and mathematicians and join in their shop talk. Pulling their earlobes as an affectionate gesture, he would, often to their intense irritation, banter along with them. On his Egyptian expedition, he had with him two mathematicians of the very first calibre: Joseph Fourier and Gaspard Monge.

On Napoleon's sudden and secret return trip to France, Monge, who was renowned for his contributions to geometry, accompanied him. It is recorded that on this voyage their ship was becalmed for weeks, and the two men discussed geometry. Perhaps Napoleon, sitting in his cabin, worried or bored, doodled out Problem 44 on a scrap of paper and showed it to Monge. Just prior to embarkation, in the garden of the military headquarters, Napoleon had expressed a hankering for scientific achievement. Fourier, Monge, the chemist Berthollet, and the amiable Madame Fourès dressed in pantaloons à la hussard, sat and listened. Napoleon reminisced about his early years: "I became a military man against my grain. I had other ambitions in my youth and believed I was destined by fate to become another Newton through my discoveries. . . . Since I have now acquired rank in the army, this dream of my youth repeatedly comes back to my mind and prompts me instinctively to spend my leisure time on Berthollet's lessons, not so much with the notion of realizing my dreams but rather to pass judgment on their worth."

Monge answered that Bonaparte had acquired enough glory outside this issue. He added that in science one could not hope to duplicate Newton's achievements since, according to a saying of Lagrange who was perhaps the leading mathematician of his day, there was only one world to discover.

Monge

"What nonsense this is!" Bonaparte heatedly replied. "There is another world, and one which may bring much glory to its discoverer. Newton has solved the problem of great masses at great distances in the universe; but this other world is that of primary molecules separated by no appreciable distance, and of their relationship. This is what I aimed at in my youth. The only use which could be made of Newton's discoveries was philosophical speculation. I saw a practical benefit to mankind in knowing the inner life of the universe."

In forming my judgment about the provenance of Napoleon's Theorem, I also knew something that the scientific world might now find outrageous, or at the very least, absurd: in 1797 Napoleon was for a while professor of geometry at The Institute. It came about in this way. One of the leading figures of the French Revolution was the mathematician Lazare Carnot (1753–1823). Carnot was also a fortification engineer, a politician, a military strategist and an administrator of great talent. A regicide, Carnot made his way up the greasy pole of revolutionary politics through the Council of Five Hundred and to the Directorate. A bit more republican than most, Carnot refused to take part in one of the Napoleonic coups d'état and was exiled. He was also kicked out of his Chair of geometry at the Institute and the position was handed over to Napoleon. Monge, for whom Napoleon was a great hero, approved the appointment. Perhaps he knew that Napoleon had discovered a new theorem in geometry and that his qualifications for the professorship were therefore not absolutely zero.

The Napoleonic connection to the theorem intrigued me. I wanted to learn more about it. A bit of preliminary scrounging yielded nothing. Biographers have been silent about the specifics of Napoleon's accomplishments in the mathematical line; in any case the books have not displayed triangles with equilateral triangles upon their sides. (But see: Joachim Fischer). I wrote to Professor Coxeter and asked him about it. He answered that he had gotten the ascription from a paper that appeared in 1937 in a Belgian mathematical journal by a certain Vincenzo Cavallaro. That was all he knew about the matter. The mystery of Napoleon's Theorem deepened, but at the time I did not have the leisure to look into it further.

4
Fourier

My first research job was at the NACA in the spring of 1944. The laboratory was staffed by old-timers in the aeronautics business plus many young draftees, hotshots in mathematics and physics who were assigned to this work as their military service. After the war, many of them left Langley Field and went on to become some of the leading scientists and technologists in the country. I worked in the Aircraft Loads Division, which carried out experimentation and analysis of the aerodynamic loading of wings and tails of fighter aircraft. We were particularly interested in what happened during maneuvers, dives, pull-outs, fish-tailing, and other evasive actions. Small holes were drilled along a cross section of a wing or the tail of a plane and tubes were inserted which were connected to pressure recorders. On the basis of these records, one could then reconstruct the profile of air pressure across the section as the aircraft performed a variety of maneuvers. From the pressure profile one went on to compute two very important aerodynamic quantities which related to wing strength and aircraft stability: the lift coefficient and the coefficient of pitching moment.

Today, a microcomputer could and probably does provide these numbers instantaneously as the experiment proceeds. The hope of theoretical aerodynamicists today is that theory plus large computers can replace experiment entirely (the so-called numerical wind tunnel), but it hasn't reached that stage. At any rate, forty years ago we depended on a laborious process of computation, and tens of thousands of man- and women-hours were devoted to it.

Our experiment was done in the following way. The pressures at the various stations across the wing or tail were plotted. The isolated values were then faired in with a french curve to give a complete pressure profile. The area under the pressure curve is essentially the lift coefficient, and the horizontal moment of that area is essentially the pitching coefficient. The process of finding of areas and moments – quite generally – goes by the mathematical name of integration, and is the second major topic into which elementary calculus is divided. Finally, as a last step, the graphical areas were obtained by using a special instrument called a planimeter. One traces the stylus of this instrument around the boundary of the area, and one can then read the area off on a dial. If the planimeter is a fancy one, and ours was, it will have two dials, the first giving area and the second giving the horizontal moment.

The super-duper planimeter of the Aircraft Loads Section of the NACA was in the permanent care of a character bearing the name of Swindells Royce — Dell for short. Dell treated the shining precision instrument with the care of a mother hen; better still, with the care of a jeweller in charge of an expensive Swiss watch, always polishing it, always locking it up when not in use. And it was good that he did so, for the planimeter was a sensitive, temperamental and rare thing. The prototype was German, the Germans in those days being the finest instrument makers. Since the war prevented their purchase the machinists at the NACA took apart the one they had and made ten copies at a cost, I was told, of $5,000 apiece. This was at a time when a Chevrolet, if you could buy one, would have cost $600.

Now it occurred to me, a fledgling mathematician, that the whole expenditure was unnecessary, that a little bit of arithmetic carefully laid out could have replaced both the drawing of the diagrams and the subsequent planimetry and would have yielded answers that were as accurate. But planimetry was the way it was done, the way it was going to be done, and I sensed that I had better shut up about it. And so I shut up and pushed the stylus around many a pressure diagram before the war ended. This experience left me with an intense interest in the theoretical aspects of approximate numerical integration.

Ten years later, in 1954, at the National Bureau of Standards in Washington, I was working as a numerical analyst and an acolyte of the SEAC, one of the earliest digital computers built in this country. As part of an extensive project, I had to do some very accurate approximate integrations in the complex plane. I thought it would be a good strategy to use a very subtle and accurate scheme derived in the early 1800's by the great German mathematician Carl Friedrich Gauss.

Prior to 1954, the Gaussian rules were known only up to sixteen points. The values had been calculated on desk calculators, an extremely laborious task. Also in the days of scientific computation done by "hand," the Gaussian rules were out of favor, as the numbers they involved were helter-skelter irrational decimals, impossible to remember and difficult to enter on a keyboard without error.

It was my plan to carry the computation beyond sixteen. At that time I was working with Phil Rabinowitz (who later became one of the first computer scientists in Israel, and professor at the Weizmann Institute). I suggested to him that we attempt the Gaussian computation on the SEAC. He was game. I anticipated that it would be desirable to work in double precision arithmetic of about thirty decimal places, and Phil, who was much more skillful at SEAC coding than I, agreed to write the portion of a code that effectuated the double precision.

But first I had to devise a numerical strategy. The n abscissas of the Gaussian integration rules are the roots of the Legendre polynomials of degree n. The weights corresponding to the abscissas are obtainable by a number of simple formulas. I proposed getting the Legendre polynomials pointwise by means of the known three-term recursion relation. I proposed getting its roots by using Newton's iterative method, starting from good approximate values. These starting values would be provided by an asymptotic formula that had been worked out in the 1930's by the Hungarian-American mathematician Gabor Szegö.

I didn't know whether this strategy would work. It might have failed for three or four different reasons. However, I was willing to try. If it worked, good; and if it didn't, well, something is always learned by failure. We could publish the failure, and other mathematicians might then be able to suggest a more successful strategy.

I wrote the code (with the exception of the double precision part). In those days the coding was done in the four address system, with fixed point arithmetic, so that scalings had to be introduced to keep numbers in bounds. I reread the code, and checked it for bugs.

I (or Phil Rabinowitz) punched up the code on teletype tape and checked that out. The tape was converted automatically to wire, and the wire cartridge was inserted in the SEAC. We manually set $n = 20$, crossed our fingers, held our breath, and pushed the button to run the program.

The SEAC computed and computed. It computed and computed; computed and computed. Our tension mounted. Finally, it started to output the Gaussian abscissas and weights. Numbers that purported to be such started spewing out at the teletype printer. The numbers had the right look and smell about them. We punched in $n = 24$ and again pushed the run button. Again, success.

The computing lab declared us "Heroes of the SEAC," a title awarded in those days to programmers whose programs ran on the first try, and for some time we had to wear appropriate medals drawn free hand on the back of used teletype paper.

This was the first electronic digital computation of the Gaussian integration rules. In the years since alternate strategies have been proposed, simplified and sharpened; and though all the theoretical questions that kept us guessing in 1955 have been decided positively, there are many problems as yet unsolved surrounding the Gauss idea. Our success and our continued interest in approximate integration led to the book on the topic of integration.

★   ★   ★

Fourier

An educated person, hearing the name Fourier, would very likely think of the French utopian socialist, François Marie Charles Fourier, who advocated that society be organized into small communes. A mathematician, an engineer, or a physicist would think rather of Jean Baptiste Joseph Fourier (1768–1830), who analyzed wave motion into its simple harmonic components. This process is so fundamental to mathematics, theoretical physics and engineering that if one could give only ten lectures on the whole of mathematics, I would suggest that one of the lectures be about the so-called Fourier analysis.

The analysis of wave motion à la Fourier involves the computation of the areas under (or integrals of) certain oscillatory curves. These areas are known as Fourier coefficients, and it has become one of the standard tasks of numerical mathematicians to compute such numbers.

In the first edition of the book on integration I wrote with Phil Rabinowitz, we put in a certain amount of information about the computation of Fourier coefficients. Even as we were working this up, a method was discovered, now known as the Fast Fourier Transform, which reduced considerably the time required for the computation of such areas. The substantial reduction in time opened up many possibilities for the computer processing of signals of all sorts. Hundreds of technical papers were written on the topic over the next decade. The IBM Company even now employs mathematicians at high salaries who think constantly about how the time may be reduced further.

When in 1974 we decided to put out an updated version of our book, it was clear that we would have to add a section about the Fast Fourier Transform. I thought I could do a perfunctory job, and so did Rabinowitz, but we wanted something better. Luckily I had a graduate student, Harvey Silverman, who was an expert both on computer hardware techniques of digital signal processing and on the theory of the Fast Fourier Transform. I asked him to write about ten pages for our book. At that time Silverman was at the Watson Labs of IBM (he is now Dean of Engineering at Brown) working on such things, and he agreed.

One of the effects of Harvey's write-up was to teach me the fundamental relationship between Fourier analysis and circulant matrices. A circulant matrix is a square array of numbers such as

$$\begin{pmatrix} 2 & 9 & 4 & 6 \\ 6 & 2 & 9 & 4 \\ 4 & 6 & 2 & 9 \\ 9 & 4 & 6 & 2 \end{pmatrix}$$

wherein the numbers in successive rows are pushed to the right by one unit and "wrapped around." The whole array of numbers is then to be taken *en bloc*. Such objects had been around in mathematics since the mid-1800's and their properties were quite well known, really, but had been forgotten and rediscovered and republished over and over again. I got interested in such matrices, learned what I could about them, discovered a few more interesting things about them on my own and ultimately, in 1979, published a little book on the topic. In looking around for simple examples to illustrate the theory, I hit on a problem that had been mentioned in the American literature since the 1930's. This is the problem of nested polygons.

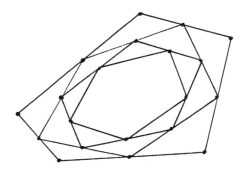

Nested polygons

Draw a random polygon. (The figure shows a polygon with five sides.) Mark the midpoints of the sides of the polygon and join the midpoints successively to form another polygon inside the first one. Keep on doing this. The successive polygons get smaller and smaller. Two questions may now be raised: can you identify in some way the point toward which the sequence of polygons converges, and can you determine the rate at which the convergence takes place? In 1950 I.J. Schoenberg at the University of Pennsylvania had shown this to be a problem of discrete Fourier analysis, and in my book I recast the problem and its solution within the context of circulant matrices.

I had hardly written up the Schoenberg material when, in a moment of illumination, without the aid of a poêle or a Glenwood stove, I realized that my Old Nemesis, Problem 44, Napoleon's Theorem, could be placed in the same context, providing one employed circulant matrices with complex imaginary entries. I introduced the 3-by-3 circulant

$$\begin{pmatrix} 1 - \omega^2 & 1 - \omega & 0 \\ 0 & 1 - \omega^2 & 1 - \omega \\ 1 - \omega & 0 & 1 - \omega^2 \end{pmatrix}$$

where $\omega = -\frac{1}{2} + \frac{\sqrt{-3}}{2}$. I called the thing N after Napoleon, and in a few lines I had my own version of Napoleon's Theorem. And I had much more besides.

The matrix N is singular; it has to be because it transforms any old triangle into an equilateral triangle. Singular though it was, I inverted it anyway, using the generalized inverse, and was able to give a geometric interpretation to what I had done. Andrew Phillips, Irving Fisher! Wake up and be proud of your student – or at least of his persistence.

At this point I thought that I had laid the ghost of Napoleon's Theorem to rest. I was wrong.

5
Neumann

I was rather tickled with my treatment of Napoleon via complex circulants and of the application I was able to make of the generalized inverse. I wanted to crow about it a little, and then I would lay the whole thing to rest. That season, when I was invited to present a guest talk at a seminar, my title was "Napoleon's Theorem and the Generalized Inverse."

I recall with particular relish the afternoon I gave this talk at the University of Vermont in Burlington. When the time came for audience questions, a man got up and, introducing himself as Professor Such and Such from Department Thus and So, announced: "I think I see the possibility of applying your work to the optimal design of triangular and hexagonal hen coops." He was not joking. After the audience had evaporated, he kept me at the blackboard for a half hour while he drew the outlines of avant-garde mathematical condominiums for chickens. I never heard from the man again, but I am quite willing to accept some credit for any additional freshness that newly-laid Vermont eggs may have.

Later the same year I received an invitation to present a series of lectures at the Summer Research Institute of the Australian Mathematical Society, to be held in Hobart, Tasmania, in January 1981. I had been in Hobart ten years before and loved it, so I accepted. On the night of December 31st, my wife and I lifted off from San Francisco International Airport and, by crossing the international date line from east to west, missed most of January 1st. For us, it was the year that wasn't ushered in. I thought at the very least there would be balloons and champagne, but QANTAS airline must have been short of money. We did get passion fruit juice for breakfast.

Naturally, one of my five talks would be "Napoleon's Theorem and the Generalized Inverse." When I arrived, Professor Rudy Lidl, a member of the organizing committee, alerted me that there would be someone in my audience who was an expert on Napoleon's Theorem and so I had better do my stuff really well.

Came the day and the hour of the talk. When I entered the

lecture room I found sitting in the first row center (unusual at any lecture, where standardly the first six rows are unoccupied) an elderly, jovial-looking fellow, wisps of white hair flying over his ears and polished billiard-ball in between them. As I lectured, this gentleman sat on the edge of his chair and followed me with gusto. His mood was infectious; it caught me up, and I think I transmitted it to the audience.

When I was through, he came up and introduced himself.

"I'm Bernhard Neumann. I enjoyed your talk greatly. Tell me, I've been wondering for years – why is Napoleon's Theorem called by that name? Do you know?"

"No I don't know. I have a couple of conjectures about the matter, if that will serve."

My wife and I stayed at the Summer Institute for several weeks, and we got to know Neumann quite well. He rented a car and drove us all over Tasmania. We learned that he had been a Napoleon buff far longer than I, and only recently had published a treatment of the theorem via linear algebra. This was essentially equivalent to what I had done, but it did not draw on the neat formalism provided by the theory of circulants, nor did he exploit the generalized inverse.

To tell Neumann's story properly I shall have to go back about a hundred years.

Electric power as a means of incandescent lighting was introduced in the early 1880's. For the first few years the power supply was all direct current. Later, the advantages of alternating current became apparent. It could be generated at low voltage, stepped up to a very high voltage where the transportation loss was minimized, and then stepped down to the very low consumer current. The first experiments in the U.S.A. in the transportation of alternating current took place in Great Barrington, Massachusetts, not far from where the famous Tanglewood Music Festival is now held.

Within a few years, in 1888, it became clear to a Croatian-American electrical engineer by the name of Nicolas Tesla, now immortalized in that the unit of magnetic flux density is called by his name, that further advantages would accrue if the current were transported not in single phase alternating current, but simultaneously in what is called three-phase alternating current. This kind of current comprises three separate sinusoidal currents of the same standard frequency (60 cycles a second in the United States) and of the same amplitude, but staggered or phased by three equal time intervals. The currents are sent over separate wires and the wires are wrapped into cables in multiples of three.

Ideally, one would like to have the three phase alternating current be "symmetric"; that is, the staggering would be precisely $\frac{1}{3}$ and $\frac{2}{3}$ of the basic period. Thinking of this in terms of the rotation of a magnet, this translates to $0°, 120°, 240°$. In practice, it is difficult to achieve this with absolute precision, and in an attempt to correct the discrepancies, theoretical studies of three-phase and polyphase alternating current systems were undertaken in the early years of this century.

The mathematical theory of alternating currents is essentially the theory of sine waves of current and voltage. It was recognized by theoreticians early on that the algebraic treatment of sine waves is greatly facilitated by the use of complex quantities, that is, numbers that involve the imaginary unit $\sqrt{-1}$, and that the basic facts about this are the de Moivre identity

$$(\cos\theta + i\sin\theta)^m = \cos m\theta + i\sin m\theta$$

and the Euler identity $e^{i\theta} = \cos\theta + i\sin\theta, \quad i = \sqrt{-1}.$

All books on alternating current theory now begin with an introductory chapter on the algebra of complex quantities, and it

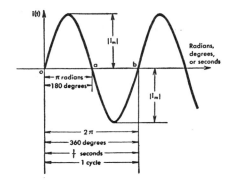

Single-phase alternating current

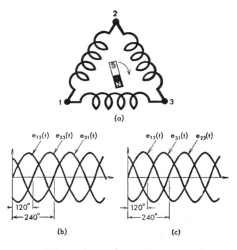

Three-phase alternating current

is amusing to recall that as late as the 1910's college mathematical commissions were arguing about whether or not undergraduate mathematical instruction should include the study of complex numbers. Part of the hesitancy derived from residual worries about the legitimacy of "imaginary" concepts such as $\sqrt{-1}$. If one could not guarantee their existential status, how could one teach them or use them? If truth be told, all mathematical concepts are "imaginary" in that they are the product of our imaginations, and today the emphasis is placed less on what mathematical objects really "are" than on how they work.

While the theory of alternate current is generally pursued via complex variables (or vectors), there are certain problems in which one might proceed graphically via two-dimensional geometry. Bernhard Neumann's father, Richard Neumann, was one of the early workers in the theory of alternating currents and a master at graphical analysis. While working on three-phase currents graphically, in 1911, Richard Neumann was led to a number of facts about triangles, plane polygons, and in particular about the equilateral triangle.

The algebraic theory of three-phase alternating current is facilitated by the use of "symmetrical component analysis," an approach which was introduced a little later by an American electrical engineer named C.L. Fortescue. In the late thirties, Richard Neumann wrote a book about symmetrical component analysis of three-phase current. The book opens with Problems 43 and 44 – Napoleon's Theorem – but it is not called by that name! Now if this does not get close to Napoleon's dream of studying primal molecules at short distances, I don't know what does.

When the proofs of the book arrived, the elder Neumann asked his son, also a crackerjack mathematician, to help him read the galleys. In the course of this tedious and burdensome work, Bernhard Neumann's fancy took wing: he asked himself, if triangles why not polygons, and if equilateral triangles, why not isosceles triangles? In this way, he arrived at a significant generalization of Napoleon's Theorem.

The Neumann family comprises at least three generations of mathematicians. Bernhard's first wife was Hannah Neumann, a distinguished algebraist, and a number of their children have also pursued the craft.

Finding his way to Australia under the pressure of Hitler's Germany, the genial and talented Neumann won recognition and honors, and now, in his retirement as Professor Emeritus of the Australian National University in Canberra, enjoys a role as the doyen of Australian mathematicians. He has been very active in formulating educational policy in Australian colleges and secondary schools.

On one of our trips we drove into Port Arthur, Tasmania, one of the original Australian penal colonies whose ruins are now a tourist attraction, and we sat down by the water for a picnic lunch. A small cruiser of the Australian Navy pulled into the channel, and Bernhard told us that he had been instrumental in putting in a course of mathematics now taken by all aspiring naval officers. He had been on naval cruises a number of times and was thus able to arrive at just what mathematics is necessary for a navy man.

From Bernhard I learned a number of new things about Napoleon's Theorem. He told me that as far as he was aware, the first mention of it as Napoleon's occurs in the work of Cavallaro in 1938. Furthermore, the first known published occurrence of the theorem is in an article by W. Fischer in the *Archiv für Mathematik und Physik* in 1863.

I toyed briefly with the notion that my Irving Fisher may have been related to this older Fischer but when I checked it out, I produced a solid line of Yankee ancestors on both sides for Irving. Bernhard told me further that the theorem was well known to the French mathematician C.A. Laissant, who wrote about it in 1877.

Phillips and Fisher might easily have picked it up from either of these early authors, as the journals in which they wrote would have been quite accessible to them at Yale.

"But Napoleon. What is the Napoleon connection?" I asked

Neumann impatiently. Neumann answered that he did not know. A few years before, he had put in a bit of effort to resolve the question. He found himself in Paris with several weeks of relaxed visiting and he thought to check the point further.

Now, in France, Napoleon is not just a general and an emperor; Napoleon is a huge industry that churns out brandy, pastry, and a million words yearly. There are libraries and libraries of Napoleonia: Napoleon and his generals, Napoleon and all the other Bonapartes, Napoleon and his women, Napoleon and the romantic movement, Napoleon and the Pope, Napoleon and the Jewish Question, Napoleon in Egypt, Napoleon at Marengo, Napoleon in Moscow, Napoleon at Elba, Napoleon at St. Helena, Napoleon and French Decorator Style, Napoleon: Was he murdered? It goes on and on and on. Napoleon is the central figure of modern European history.

Neumann turned up nothing about Napoleon and his geometrical theorem. His blood quickened when he found *"Souvenirs sur Monge et ses rapports avec Napoléon,"* published in Paris, 1853, but this lead fizzled out. It contained nothing of relevance.

Neumann asked for my opinion. I answered that I'd turned up nothing. "But I have several conjectures. In the first place, the theorem might have been named in honor of Napoleon, just as the Emperor Concerto and the Eroica were composed by Beethoven and not by Napoleon. Assuming this, then, reasonable candidates for authorship of the theorem would be either Carnot or Monge. I think Carnot is the most likely. Monge was infatuated with Napoleon and idolized him; if he had wanted to honor his Emperor, he would have attached his name to a more glorious and grandiose result. After all, he had acquiesced in naming Napoleon Professor of Geometry. Carnot, on the other hand, was rather independent of Napoleon, and their relationship was touch and go. He might just

Fischer: Ein geometrischer Satz.

XXVIII.

Ein geometrischer Satz.

Von

Herrn Gymnasial-Oberlehrer *W. Fischer*
in Kempen.

Satz. Beschreibt man über den Seiten eines Dreiecks gleichseitige Dreiecke und verbindet die Mittelpunkte derselben, so schliessen die Verbindungslinien ein gleichseitiges Dreieck ein.

Es hat dieser Satz Gültigkeit, sowohl wenn die gleichseitigen Dreiecke nach aussen hin, als auch wenn dieselben nach innen über den Seiten eines Dreiecks beschrieben sind. Betrachten wir zunächst den ersten Fall.

Bezeichnet ABC ein beliebiges Dreieck, über dessen Seiten gleichseitige Dreiecke beschrieben sind, und benennt man den Mittelpunkt des über der Seite BC beschriebenen gleichseitigen Dreiecks mit α, eben so den Mittelpunkt des über der Seite AC beschriebenen gleichseitigen Dreiecks mit β und den des gleichseitigen Dreiecks über AB mit γ: so ist, wenn man die Linien $\alpha\beta$, $\alpha\gamma$ und $\beta\gamma$ zieht, Dreieck $\alpha\beta\gamma$ ein gleichseitiges. Fällt man etwa von dem Punkte C aus auf $\alpha\beta$ die Senkrechte CD, welche innerhalb des Dreiecks ABC fallen möge, und verlängert dieselbe um sich selbst bis zum Punkte E, so ist, wenn man noch C mit α und E mit α verbindet:

$$\triangle CD\alpha \cong \triangle ED\alpha;$$

eben so, wenn man C und E mit β verbindet,

First published instance of Problem 44 known to the author – 1863 have put Napoleon's name on this little inky-dinky bit of mathematics so as to deflate the Emperor. Moreover, Carnot made many contributions to the geometry of the triangle, while Monge did not."

These were my historical conjectures. I also told Bernhard that I thought it almost certain that the result was known to the famous Italian physicist and mathematician Evangelista Torricelli (1608–1647), who appears to have written on what I have called Problem 43, and very likely known also to the equally famous French lawyer and mathematician Pierre de Fermat (1601–1665). Fermat posed the problem of finding that point which minimizes the sum of its distances to three given points, and the solution is given by the construction of Problem 43. Torricelli knew about these matters.

I conjectured further that the whole question was known in antiquity, and that eventually a manuscript would turn up in the library of a Greek orthodox monastery in the Near East, which would be a 17th century Greek translation (faked to appear in 10th century Greek, for unknown reasons) of an 8th century Arabic commentary on Pappus which contains Problem 44 and which claims for it Pythagorean origin. *Si non è vero è bene trovato.*

I told Bernard that in addition to all this, I had two graphical conjectures as to the Napoleonic connection, and when I got back to Providence, I sent him the following four pictures:

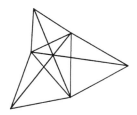 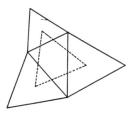

Fortifications or Napoleon's Theorem?

Magnificently caparisoned and panached,
Napoleon discusses mathematics en route to victory.

6
Cavallaro

I got back to Providence from Hobart and sent Neumann the pictures immediately. It was clear that meeting him had rekindled my interest in the Napoleon connection. The work of Neumann's father and his fellow electrical engineers had lifted the theorem from a high school exercise to a statement of some significance in the theory of power transmission. Who knows but that in the future, Napoleon's Theorem might be found to have application to theories of technologies as yet unborn?

To get closer to the Napoleon enigma there was no point in reading historical material on the Emperor. I trusted Neumann to have done his work well. I would go back to the work of Cavallaro where the first ascription known to Neumann occurred. Perhaps I would find a clue there.

Looking up the work of Vincenzo Cavallaro for the year 1938, I found the reference to Napoleon. A footnote: *"Théorème attribué à Napoléon Bonaparte."* That was all. Nothing more. Attribué by whom? When? Where? Under what circumstances? Not a clue. Cavallaro wrote from Cefalù, a small village on the north shore of Sicily; if he had written from a small village in Corsica I might have said "Aha" and gone back to the life of Napoleon.

I checked out other papers by Cavallaro. The first I found was dated 1927. I looked at the papers he wrote after 1937. In several of the papers I found the same cryptic remark: *"Théorème dite de Napoléon."* That was all.

One afternoon not long ago my phone rang, and a man identifying himself as Ed Miller said he was calling up because he had heard I was a mathematician. He had a question to ask me.

"I am. Ask away."

Miller said that he was a roofer in town, and he had a roof whose area he wanted to estimate. He recalled that there were mathematical ways of doing this and had known them in high school, but he had forgotten them and would I help him.

It seemed to me that any roofer worthy of his trade could at a single glance estimate the area of a roof to within two packages of shingles, whereas any professional mathematician would surely make an awful hash of it. I didn't want to insist on this point over the phone, hoping to be helpful, so I pursued the matter.

"What kind of a roof is it?"

"What do you mean, what kind of a roof is it? It's a roof. A roof on a house."

"I mean what kind of surfaces is the roof made up of? Triangles, rectangles? And how are they put together? I can't give you a formula unless you tell me."

"Oh, I see. Well, the roof has triangles."

"Just triangles, no rectangles? How many triangles are there? How are they joined up?"

"There are four of them. It's like a pyramid. But not a pyramid in Egypt, a pyramid with four triangles."

I let the Egypt remark pass and went on with my inquisition. I call it that because I could hear over the phone that I was walking close to the limits of Ed Miller's knowledge of geometrical nomenclature.

"These four triangles, what shape are they? Are they equilateral triangles like one sees in some high pitched garage roofs or are they isosceles triangles? I've got to know."

No reply from my caller.

"Well, let's look at it another way: You've got four triangles. Find the area of each triangle and add them up."

"How do you do that?"

"The area of a triangle is one half the base times its altitude."

"My triangles don't have an altitude."

"Don't have an altitude? All triangles have an altitude."

"I tell you this roof has no altitude."

"Well, if it doesn't we will have to supply the triangles with altitudes and then do the computation."

At this point, Mr. Miller, feeling that he had had quite enough with this professor nut who was asking him to go to an altitude supplier and run up a bill, said he didn't understand, but would come over and talk to me personally.

Ed Miller never showed up, and I began to wonder if my caller was a hoaxing student. It was vacation time, so I doubt it.

Yes, Mr. Miller, every triangle has an altitude, and if you don't see it in your figure you supply it by putting in what is called a construction line.

In fact, Mr. Miller, every triangle has not only one altitude, it has *three* altitudes, and these altitudes, miraculously, always meet in a common point. This is true no matter what shape the triangle is, whether it is an equilateral triangle or an isosceles triangle or a common, ordinary, garden-variety, no-account triangle, also known as a scalene triangle.

The point at which the three altitudes meet is called the orthocenter of the triangle, and was known to Euclid, if not to earlier mathematicians. As far as I am aware, this fact is of absolutely no consequence to the roofing industry. The story of the roofer brings me closer though to the substance of Vincenzo Cavallaro's article written in 1938 in Cefalù.

The orthocenter of a triangle is one of four remarkable points related to a triangle. The other three are the centroid (the center of gravity), the incenter – the center of the inscribed circle – and the circumcenter – the center of the circumscribed circle. In an equilateral triangle which has many symmetries, all these four points coalesce into one and the same point.

What is striking also about these remarkable points is that, just as the orthocenter is the common intersection of the three altitudes, the centroid is the common intersection of the three medians, the incenter is the common intersection of the three angle bisectors, and the circumcenter is the common intersection of the three perpendicular bisectors of the three sides.

All of this was known in antiquity. Throughout the 1800's until perhaps fifty years ago, there was a small but steady interest in discovering or working out new facts about triangles. Within this so-called "geometry of the triangle," many remarkable points now named after their discoverers came to light, and the peculiarities of these points were elucidated. The late 18th and 19th centuries saw the emergence of the nine point circle, the Lemoine point, the Brocard points, the Euler point, and a dozen others.

Dreiecksgeometrie (Dreieck = triangle), as the Germans called it, passed through three national phases. First there was a French phase. This was followed by a German phase, followed again by a French phase. What is *Dreieckgeometrie?* Well, first and foremost, it is the study of remarkable points and of their interrelation. But just what constitutes a remarkable point, no one has yet been able to say or to axiomatize.

The culmination of this work occurred in a 100-page survey article written for the great *Encyklopädie der Mathematischen Wissen-schaften* in the spring of 1914. By the fall of 1914, one of the coauthors of the article, a young man of thirty-two, fell on the field of battle. So also *Dreiecksgeometrie* died, not in combat, but of inner exhaustion. Its melody lingers on. In the United States as recently as twenty years ago, courses in advanced plane geometry, often called simply "college geometry," were taught whenever there happened to be

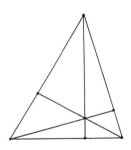

The three altitudes of a triangle
meet at the orthocenter.

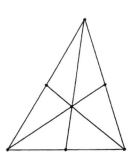

The three medians of a triangle
meet at the centroid.

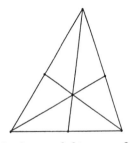

The three angle bisectors of a triangle
meet at the incenter.

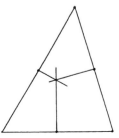

The three perpendicular bisectors
of the sides of a triangle
meet at the circumcenter.

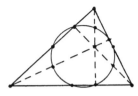

The nine point circle.

a virtuoso on the triangle.

It is within this tradition that Napoleon's Theorem falls, and also the work of Cavallaro. What is Cavallaro's paper all about? In brief, it gives a relationship between the circumcenter, the nine point center, the Brocard points and the Napoleon triangles of a given triangle. So as not to snow the reader who is not adept at mathematical nomenclature and symbolism, I will take it slowly and introduce the cast of characters one by one.

Take a triangle, any old kind of a triangle. We will designate it by T.

α) Through the vertices of T, we may draw a unique circle. This circle has a center. Call it O. This is the circumcenter of T.

β) The triangle T has three altitudes and each altitude has a foot. Pass a circle through these three feet. This is the so-called nine point circle of the triangle T. It is called the nine point circle because it also passes through the three midpoints of the sides of T as well as the three midpoints of the segments of the altitudes from the vertices to the orthocenter. What a multiplication of miracles! Call the center of the nine point circle O_9.

γ) Designate the vertices of T by A, B, and C. Pass a circle through A and B tangent to BC at B. Pass a circle through B and C tangent to CA at C. Pass a circle through C and A tangent to AB at A. Then (another miracle) these three circles intersect at a common point. Call it Ω. This is the first Brocard point of T.

Why is this a miracle? Well, three circles need not intersect at all, as with ⚬⚬. Or two of them may intersect and the other one not, as with ⚭. The three may intersect two by two as with the famous beer symbol ⊛. If three circles go through a common point ⊗, it's got to be a rare event.

Pass a circle through A and C tangent to BC at C.

Pass a circle through B and A tangent to CA at A.

Pass a circle through C and B tangent to CA at B.

Then (you guessed it!) these three circles miraculously pass through another common point. Call it Ω'. This is the second Brocard point of T.

δ) Join Ω and Ω' by a straight line. Call its midpoint W.

ϵ) Hark back to Napoleon's theorem. An equilateral triangle was created by erecting three equilateral triangles *outwardly* on the sides of T. Call this triangle the Napoleon triangle of T, and let the length of its side be designated by L.

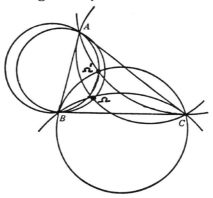

The Brocard points

We might just as well have erected equilateral triangles *inwardly* on the sides of T. It would have resulted (miraculously!) in a second or inner Napoleon triangle. Call the length of its side L'.

ζ) Designate by OW the distance from O to W. Designate by O_9W the distance from O_9 to W.

Now, for the final miracle and Cavallaro's theorem:

η) $OW/O_9W = (L/L') + (L'/L)$.

Triangle geometry can be fun and it can be ingenious. Some mathematicians deplore it saying that its devoid of new ideas, a dead

46

end, nothing more than high school geometry gone crazy or gone rotten. One person's mould may be another person's Camembert. The subject maintains a kind of a shadowy existence in the private domain of mathematical hobbyists and serves as a warning that any discipline may be exhausted by overdevelopment and equally well may be revitalized by the perception of new interrelations.

Even as I was fussing with pen, paper, scissors and scotch tape, putting this manuscript together, Jill Hellendale, friend of my wife and myself for many years, was by strange coincidence or kismetic predestination visiting Cefalù. She wrote to us, "Cefalù is an interesting little fishing village on the Tyrrhenian Sea on the north coast of Sicily, about an hour's drive from Palermo. It nestles at the base of an enormous rock; to the west is the sweeping Bay of Imerese. One of the finest Norman cathedrals dominates Cefalù, and the mosaic Christ Pantocrator in the apse exhibits searching-eyed gentleness.

"Cefalù is an ideally handy spot for winter-weary dwellers in Northern Europe, and they have found it. Its days as a small village are numbered, as you can see from the long list of hostelries. So far, the harborscape under the rock remains unviolated, but the view from the Night Club Heucaliptus exhibits apartment blocks that have started to rise outside the Old Town. It's only a question of time before someone will buy up contiguous buildings and put up bland, balconied hi-rises that will disfigure the breathtaking view."

If I had known that Jill was going to be in Cefalù I would have written to her: "When you get there, look up Cavallaro for me and ask him about Napoleon. There's a reasonable possibility he's alive. The first paper he wrote that I'm aware of was in 1927. Assuming he was, let us say, twenty at the time, that would make him seventy-five now. If he's not alive, find his widow. See if there is a *Nachlass* (residuary manuscript). If there is, cable, and I'll come and examine it. If you can't find the widow, go to Palermo, hire a detective and have him locate the next of kin. If not, perhaps there was a mistress. Perhaps two maiden nieces have inherited their old uncle's papers. Make them an offer of $100 for the whole mildewed batch. Tell the detective to be discreet, for if it gets noised about that a crazy American is bidding for papers, the price will surely rise to 1,000,000,000 lira. Use your judgment and act rapidly, for, by the searching-eyed gentleness of Christ Pantocrator of Cefalù, I mean to know how Napoleon came by his theorem, or how the theorem came by Napoleon."

This was so much daydreaming derived from reading too many thrillers. It would yield nothing. The right way to go about detective work is quietly, consistently, systematically, ploddingly, to examine the writings of the many authors who wrote on the "modern theory of the triangle" in the 19th century. As the thrillers assure us, detective work is 95% dull legwork, finding which London hotel John Smith checked into on the night of November 10. This was a job for Rumplestilskin and not for the miller's daughter. Nor for me.

7
Douglas and Chang

In the late 1950's, when Washington was the center of the world and the National Bureau of Standards there was one of the leading institutions for the development of scientific computer strategies, I, as head of the Numerical Analysis Section, did my fair share of showing VIPs around. Sometimes I had plenty of advance notice. This was the case in 1958 when the first post-Stalin delegation of Russian mathematicians came through, and I laid on a full tea at 10:30 AM with cakes and jam. Much more often, though, odd people would just pop in on me. One afternoon there was a knock on my door and when I'd said "Come in," I found a short, stocky Peruvian, of dark red complexion, wearing a magnificent woolen poncho and a strange bowler hat. He was obviously of Inca descent and looked as though he'd just stepped out of a page of *National Geographic*. He spoke English very decently and announced that he had been sent by his government to find out all there was to know about computers and numerical analysis. He pulled out a long set of credentials and identifications and I was impressed. I told him that his order was a very tall one, but if he would sit down we could talk. And talk he did, not I, about Washington and how it differed from Lima, about how he couldn't buy a certain brand of I now forget what, about how the oldest university in the western hemisphere was the University of Lima and not Harvard, and how. . . . After an hour of this, he toddled off very cheerfully and knocked on someone else's door.

One morning, it must have been in the early sixties, there was a knock on my door and a man came in and told me his name was Jesse Douglas. As I recall it he was a chunky sort of a man and spoke with a strong New York City accent. He told me he was passing through Washington and thought he would come up and talk with me. I had never met him before, but I knew that there was a Jesse Douglas who, in the early thirties, had made a great splash in the mathematical world by his solution of the minimal surface problem. I asked my visitor if he was *this* Jesse Douglas, and he said he was.

It was a mistake for me to have asked this question and I knew it within minutes; the topic was a "King Charles' Head" for the man. The minimal surface problem (also called Plateau's Problem) has to do with the existence of a surface of minimal area that is bounded by

49

a curved loop. In 1849 the Belgian physicist Joseph Plateau tackled the problem by making loops out of wire and dipping them in a soap solution. A soap film forms inside the wire loop and contracts itself into a position of stable equilibrium which corresponds to a surface of relative minimum area.

In the nineteen century, the problem was solved for many specific shapes of loops. (The minimal surfaces for soap films are visually interesting only when the loop does not lie entirely in a plane.) But what was at stake mathematically, and what was so difficult, was the proof of the existence of the solution under very general conditions as to loop shape. The problem defied some of the most brilliant mathematicians of the period: Riemann, Weierstrass, Schwarz, to name a few.

In 1931, Jesse Douglas, in a brilliant breakthrough, cracked the problem. His moment of glory was brief: the achievement was soon clouded by acrimony and recrimination about questions of priority. A solution, obtained simultaneously and independently, was published in 1930 by the Hungarian (later: American) mathematician Tibor Rado. For an hour or more, in a mixture of mathematical exposition and monomaniacal vituperation, Douglas told me of the slights and injuries he had received at the hands of mathematicians X, Y and Z.

I was wearied by Douglas' monomania. Priority, credit, honor, assertions of comparative brilliance, who did what first and where – why did it all matter? Are we not all interlinked in the creative process? Is there not a kind of socialism of discovery and invention, a Fourierism of the creative faculties?

This is true enough; yet, apparently, it does matter. What is at stake is not money or patent rights, but, within a tiny circle, achievement, position, recognition, perhaps even medals, glory and, for the very, very few, immortality.

Mathematics is created by individuals. It is not found on tablets carried down from Mount Sinai, nor is it found in a basket abandoned on church steps, nor is it the product of nameless and faceless committees. Being human, we want to identify wherever we can the individuals who were responsible for bringing it forth. If we ourselves are responsible, we want the world to know about it. We want to crow a little. If we are honest about it, we crow while also admitting that "we stand on the shoulders of giants." If we are still more honest, as we crow, we remember the Andrew Phillipses of our youth and the whole scientific milieu within which we work.

I thought to deflect Douglas' conversation; I finally broke in, stopped him short, and asked him what kind of thing he had worked on after Plateau's problem. He thought a moment and said, "Do you know this little fact from elementary geometry? Take any triangle and erect equilateral triangles on its sides. The centers of the equilateral triangles themselves form an equilateral triangle." Did I know it? Old Nemesis! Did I know the back of my hand? I admitted that I knew the result, but I didn't want to go into a long narrative about just what my relation to it was. Douglas went on: "Well, I found a generalization. Very nice. Very beautiful. That's something that they can't take away from me." He went over to my blackboard to elucidate.

Roughly speaking, Douglas showed me how, if one starts from a polygon of n sides, then by erecting certain isoceles triangles of a certain base angle over and over again, one arrives at $n - 1$ regular polygons of n sides. At this level of generality, a geometric figure is not apt to be illuminating; the push of the theorem really comes from the algebra. I didn't know it at the time, and if I had known it I would have said nothing, but Douglas' theorem which no one could take from him was arrived at almost simultaneously and independently by Bernhard Neumann 3000 miles across the sea. Call him Ichabod, for the glory hath departed. This kind of coincidence is, as we have seen, not infrequent, and makes one think about the exact role that individual genius plays in the history of ideas.

Time marched on. The United states ping-pong team went to China in 1971. Henry Kissinger then followed the team, and President Richard Nixon followed Kissinger. Before long, several hundred Chinese mathematicians, many of them rescued from extended rustication during the Mao Tse Tung moratorium on scientific research, were knocking on our door as visiting scholars. A knock on my door at Brown came not so many months ago, and a Professor Geng-Zhe Chang of National China University, a man whom I had never met before, entered. He had come to work with me for a few months, and before long he placed in my hands a manuscript that contained a circulant formulation of the Napoleon-Douglas-Neumann Theorem, and of the symmetric component analysis of Fortescue and Richard Neumann.

But why Napoleon? How did Napoleon get into the act?

Chang did not know.

Neumann did not know.

Coxeter did not know.

I do not know.

8
Descartes' Melon

Descartes dreamed. At the end of his first dream he saw a melon from a far-off land. Subsequent philosophers and commentators – anti-Cartesians, no doubt – have laughed at the melon. Even as Descartes dreamed, he interpreted the dream and later told us what his interpretation was. Modern dream men, Sigmund Freud included, have not found reason to dispute his reading.

The melon, said Descartes, represents the pleasures of contemplation in solitude.

This story is at an end. But only temporarily, I suppose, for it can go on and on. In mathematics there is never a final revelation or resolution.

Mathematics is pure form, pure pattern. It is abstraction and generalization. It is logical deduction and naked reason. It is doubt and certainty, certainty and doubt. It is discovery and invention. It is the world of experience impinging on the world of the imagination.

It is an arena where individual skill, imagination, intuition, and fantasy are pitted against the stubbornness of mathematical fact. It displays an unfolding and interlocking of ideas. It passes them from person to person, from generation to generation. It proceeds in cycles from the world outside to the world inside the individual, and back again to the outside. The process is without beginning and without end.

Mathematics is the possible and the impossible, the finite and the infinite, locked in tension. The creation of mathematics is done in concert and in community, and it is done much more intensely in solitude.

For those who do it, it is the sweet melon of Descartes.

$$\text{ὅπερ ἔδει δεῖξαι}$$

9
Epilogue

This chapter is a much-expanded version of a talk I gave in 1981 and wrote up shortly after. In the intervening years, the interest of the mathematical community in Napoleon's Theorem has never flagged. Among the variety of writings that can be listed are (a) new and related mathematical material and approaches including computer approaches, (b) discovery of early statements of Napoleon's Theorem, and (c) speculations as to the attribution of the theorem to Napoleon Bonaparte.

In 1992, Professor John Wetzel published an article mainly about (a), but dealing, en passant, with (b) and (c). The earliest statement of Napoleon of which I am now aware (through Wetzel) is in Rutherford's article of 1825. It remains absolutely amazing to me that the theorem is not to be found in the classical Greek mathematical literature.

The earliest known attribution to Napoleon that I know of (again through Wetzel) is in Faifofer's textbook, where it appears as a comment to a Problem No. 494: *"Teorema proposto per la dimostrazione da Napoleone a Lagrange."* An earlier edition of Faifofer's book contains neither the comment nor the problem.

A convincing connection between the theorem and the Emperor has yet to be found.

54

II

Carpenter and the Napoleon Ascription

Carpenter

1
Introduction

I could never completely abandon the search for the connection. This lovely theorem in elementary geometry had been attributed to Napoleon!

Why Napoleon? How did Napoleon get into the act?

Coxeter in Toronto did not know.

Neumann in Canberra did not know.

Chang in Hefei did not know.

Wetzel in Urbana did not know.

Scriba in Hamburg did not know.

At Scriba's suggestion, I wrote to Joachim Fischer in Berlin, a man who wrote a large book on Napoleon and science.

Fischer did not know.

I do not know.

But I'm about to tell you anyway.

My answer may surprise you. It may be a fantasy, but a fantasy that involves historical people. I'll take it very slowly, for in addition to my answer I would like to tell you how I arrived at the answer. If you are an impatient type, you may, of course, skip right to the end, as some people do when they're reading novels or detective stories.

Alex Carpenter led me to the answer, and I must therefore introduce you to him. Merely introduce? No. Much more than that. I intend to produce a mini-biography.

Alexander Sedgewick Carpenter (1920–1991) was my friend and my occasional literary guru. Carpenter called himself a Classicist, an Arabist, a Sanskritist, a historian of ancient science. I like to tell people that Carpenter knew everything worth knowing prior to 600 AD. His domain of knowledge extended from the Orkneys to

Burma. If pressed, I might raise the date and say he knew everything prior to 1700 and throw in Tibet for good measure.

Carpenter fascinated me and still does. He was a marvel, an oddball. I would like to show you the sort of thing that was in his mind, to give you a guided tour, like a busload of rubberneckers being driven to the Acropolis, of what he thought about, how he operated, what his methods were.

Carpenter once told me a story – he was an inveterate fabulist – that he got from the book by John Aubrey about a certain Thomas Allen, a mathematician and astrologer born in 1542. Allen had the reputation of being a conjurer. He kept a lot of mathematical instruments in his room (rare and suspicious objects in those days) and he claimed, so his servants said, that spirits walked up and down his staircase like bees.

One time Allen was staying in the country at the home of a friend. His reputation must have preceded him and penetrated to the servants' quarters. I now quote from Aubrey's *Brief Lives*:

"He happened to leave his watch in the chamber window. The maids came in to make the bed. At that time watches were great rarities. They heard a thing in a case cry 'Tick, Tick, Tick.' They concluded it was a devil, took it by the string and threw it out of the window into the moat to drown the devil. The string got caught on the branch of an elder tree that grew out of the moat, so that the good old gentleman got his watch again. This convinced the maids that it really was the devil."

Well, I should like to show what made Carpenter tick, tick, tick. I would like to tell you how my friendship with him led to my solution of the ascription of Napoleon's Theorem. The solution itself will occupy but little space, a few pages at most. But if I were to get to it directly you would miss an introduction to one of the most remarkable scholars I have known, and to some of the most singular stories, personal and legendary, that I have heard.

How did I meet Carpenter? It was like this.

2
The False Cryptographer

Somewhere along the twisted path called "My Career," I picked up the reputation of being a code breaker. This is not the case; I would be hard put to solve the Jumble in the morning paper. The facts are these: I have been interested in cryptography since childhood. I know a fair amount about the techniques involved. I have known many professional mathematicians who were engaged in it during World War II, including the great Arne Buerling, a Swedish mathematician of extraordinary brilliance who cracked some of the German codes. I have devised ciphers, I have given courses on the topic, and some of my students have found jobs with the National Security Agency, but I have never once deciphered a message of any significance. I know the theory and shy away from the practice. Perhaps it's being disingenuous when I say that I see no reason for the aura of code-breaker to have clung to me. Nonetheless, deserved or not, this reputation led me to receive the following message in the early 1970's:

Dear Professor Davis:

I understand you are a cryptographer. If so, I have an Elizabethan puzzle that might amuse you. Could you stop by my office some day?

Sincerely,
Alex Carpenter
303 Ashcroft Hall
Brown University

A year prior to receiving Carpenter's note, I had been teaching a course in computer science, and Domenic Capelli, a student in that course, had asked me to suggest an honors project for him. On my desk was a recent book on mathematical cryptography by Professor Abraham Sinkov. I gave it to Capelli and suggested that he take the ideas of the book and computerize them. The topic clicked. Within a week Capelli had absorbed the whole book and was writing sophisticated programs for encoding and decoding.

In the spring semester, Capelli asked me for another topic along the same line. I put him on to the problem of determining the authorship of the unsigned Federalist Papers: were they written by Hamilton or Madison? This question had just been "settled" in a book by Frederick Mosteller of Harvard. Capelli zipped through the book in no time and reconfirmed Mosteller's conclusion that Madison was the author. I then gave him stories by Robert Benchley and Stephen Leacock (with the authors' names stripped off) and asked him to distinguish which was which. I suppose that through Capelli's work the word got around the campus that I was an expert cryptographer. I went to see Carpenter anyway on false pretenses.

Ashcroft Hall is a dark red brick Victorian Ugly at the opposite end of the campus from my building. It nearly fell victim to the wreckers' ball. As soon as tentative plans were announced to replace it with a Modern Ugly, the friends and lovers of Ashcroft surfaced and formed a Save Ashcroft Committee. The Committee won. Three years later I was knocking on the heavy oak door of Room 303, miraculously preserved.

A man of about fifty opened it and identified himself as Alexander Carpenter.

"Won't you sit down?"

I looked around Room 303. Short of the library stacks, I had never seen so many books piled into a single room. Where could I sit down? Every square inch of horizontal surface was covered. Books, papers, notes, manuscripts, all congregated in a Walpurgisnacht of random and chaotic disorder. The only available chair was piled three feet high with the musty and caking volumes of a decayed concordance. Underneath the chair, like Cerberus, a nondescript brown mutt eyed me with suspicion and guarded the concordance.

Carpenter figured out my dilemma and brought in a student's seat from an adjacent classroom.

The previous summer I had been to London and seen *Brief Lives*, a brilliant one-man show performed by the actor Roy Dotrice. The play is a monologue delivered by John Aubrey, an eccentric 17th-century antiquary and accumulator of biographical oddities. The stage setting was a masterpiece of gothic dust and chaos, of books, minerals, specimens, armor, spiderwebs and unwashed crockery.

"Your office reminds me of the set for *Brief Lives*. Minus the spider webs, of course.

"Oh, you like Aubrey?"

"Yes. Very much indeed."

"Great man, John Aubrey. Great man. I have spiders too. There are spells to keep them away, but they are not effective."

And with this improbable conversation, an enduring friendship began.

Carpenter went over to the bookcase and took down a book with a photograph stuck in the pages. He handed the picture to me. What I saw were five or six lines of writing in a kind of script that was totally unfamiliar; a sequence of dashes and odd scratches of the pen.

"I should like to get this deciphered," he told me.

"This is in code?"

"I believe so."

"Who wrote it?"

"Simon Forman."

"Who's he?"

"An Elizabethan physician and astrologer. These are probably sheets from a diary or a casebook of Forman's."

"Where'd you get it?"

"From the Bodleian Library. There's lots of Forman's stuff in the Bodleian. Some of it's been deciphered. There's an Englishman by the name of A.L. Rouse who thinks he can identify Shakespeare's "Dark Lady" on the basis of some of Forman's medical notes. Forman had a practice among the aristocrats. Rouse wrote a book about it."

"Who was the Dark Lady?"

"Rouse thinks it's. . . . Well, read his book, it's lots of fun. Crazy."

"Why do you want this stuff deciphered?"

"It may tell us a lot about medical and astrological practice four hundred years ago. They were intertwined, you know. If you went to a physician four hundred years ago, the first thing he did – if you had money that is – is cast your horoscope. Then he would take a urine specimen."

"Just like today. Only the horoscopes are not covered by medical plans."

"You're right. It may come to it, though. What I believe is that the code conceals a record of Simon Forman's sexual activity. He was a man who believed deeply in the astrological order of things. If the system of nativity horoscopes he used did not give good results, then Forman thought that this was due to unusual events which introduced perturbations and discrepancies from the normal order. To study these unusual events and correlate them Forman kept a notebook jotting down his sexual activity. That's my conjecture."

At this point, I confessed and explained my deficiencies as a cryptographer. However, I said that my hot shot student Domenic

Capelli would make meatballs of it in ten minutes.

"I doubt it. The writing is much faded. It's probably in a simple transposition cipher, but the cryptographer will have to realize that it can't be as simple as that. It's full of short, telegraphic language, full of abbreviations, full of medical, alchemical, astrological terms. And it's very likely written in a mixture of Elizabethan English, French, Latin, Greek, all of the pig variety. Possibly even Hebrew and Chaldean. One doesn't know where one language begins and the other leaves off. After all, it's a series of notes jotted down rapidly in a very personal cipher."

Carpenter proved correct. A month went by and Capelli hadn't come in with the plaintext, as cryptographers call a decipherment.

"Running into problems?" I asked Capelli.

"No. No problems. I just haven't been able to get to it. I've been climbing."

"Climbing? Where do you climb. In New Hampshire?"

"No, not mountains. I climb walls. I climbed Redfield Library. I've climbed Andrews. Last week I climbed the dome of the State House."

"They let you do this? You are the Human Spider?"

"No they don't let me. I have to climb in the early hours. Three to five A.M."

A month later, Capelli went down to New York to appear on the "What's My Line" T.V. Show. An honest boy with honest emotions, he lost, and when he came home depressed, I excused him from the Forman assignment.

I sent the code off to Professor Abe Sinkov in Phoenix, Arizona. Sinkov kept it for several months and then wrote me that he needed more material to work with. After all, five lines of text is not much. At that point Carpenter was in Mysore, effectively incommunicado, and as I write these lines many years later, the residuary Forman material in the Bodleian remains undeciphered.

3
Alexander Sedgwick Carpenter

Alexander Sedgwick Carpenter was born under the sign of Leo in Contoocook, a small village in New Hampshire, to a family that had roots in the area for at least seven generations. His grandfather was raised on a farm and never gave it up completely. He worked from time to time as a loom fixer in the famous (for quality) Contoocook Woolen Mills. Carpenter's father ran an agency for trucks and large farm equipment, and Carpenter grew up in fairly comfortable circumstances. In contrast to the average village boy and to his own two older brothers, he was not interested in sports or in the outdoor life that abounds in New Hampshire. He was a reversion, perhaps, to his grandfather's grandfather, a previous Alexander Carpenter, who was a minister in Contoocook in the 1830's.

My Alex took to books early. He was sent to Phillips Exeter Academy, as he tells the story, partly because his seventh grade teacher suggested it to his mother, and partly because his father thought that Exeter might force him into more athletics than he might otherwise have gotten in the Union High School. But how could it have? He came to Exeter knowing as much if not more Latin and Greek than the teachers in Union High, and he was well into Sanskrit. He was led to this partly by reading Ralph Waldo Emerson, and he is therefore one of a long line of New England Yankees who have found the Vedic traditions a considerable suet ball to nibble on during the cold New Hampshire winters.

By the time Carpenter matriculated at Harvard, he had under his belt (if that is where one stores knowledge) all the history and all the European languages, dead or alive, offered at Exeter. He was more than a bit of a wunderkind, and he knew it, though he says that he was not of the obnoxious variety. As a freshman at Harvard, he signed up for Advanced Sanskrit and Arabic. He did his course work quietly. He suffered through the swimming course and swimming exam without which he could not be admitted into the Fellowship of Educated Men at graduation time.

Carpenter majored in Classics, of course, and sat at the feet of Werner Jaeger, Arthur Darby Nock, Harry Wolfson, Francis Cleaves (a man who was too learned to have students, too detached to ask for a raise, and who made ends meet by gift wrapping in the Jordan Marsh department store over the Christmas season), and the other suns and stars of the first magnitude whose light illuminated the ancient world. As relaxation from a curriculum that he was forced to take in order to pile up credits, Carpenter audited courses in the history of science.

I once asked Carpenter what had been the high spot of his career at Exeter. It turned out not to be a congenial question and his answer was not exactly to the point. But it led to a stimulating recollection.

"There was a man called Uncle Eddie who ran an athletic goods store near the main gate. His shop was a jumble of suits and shirts and sneakers and tennis rackets and Milky Ways. The guy pretended to be an old New England Yankee and ran his shop in the style of the 1850's. Actually it was 1920's style and he'd never cleaned it out since the partial eclipse of 1923. When the students came in, Uncle Eddie contrived to tease them in some way. Still, it was the most popular store in town, because the students had unlimited credit there, including cash, after Eddie had checked out out their parents with the school.

"One day I came in to buy a pair of socks or something, and Uncle Eddie said to me, 'One from two makes three. Answer me that.'

"This was trivial, I'd heard it when I was seven or eight. So I answered him with another riddle, 'What goes on four, on two, and then on three. Answer me that.' The Riddle of the Sphinx. From Oedipus. Sophocles. But I asked Eddie my riddle in the original Greek."

"Oh, a wise guy kid, eh?"

"You might say that. Uncle Eddie was a constant irritation."

"What about high spots at Harvard?"

"One of the first things that impressed me was the terrific memories of some of the guys there. Werner Jaeger collated versions of the New Testament practically out of his head. Arthur Darby Nock could rattle off page after page of P. G. Wodehouse and then do the same for the Egyptian *Book of the Dead*.

"Once I heard Harry Wolfson give a lecture at the Byzantine Institute at Dumbarton Oaks in Washington – this was some years after I had gotten out. He gave a one and a half hour lecture on Aristotle's *De Motu Planetorum*, complicated geometry and astronomy, all without lecture notes and in five or six original languages. A virtuoso performance if there ever was one.

"In professional work, memory is important because it allows us to bring into the forefront of consciousness many relevant facts and statements and allows us to construct a coherent picture of the subject. This cannot be done by consultation of reference books, although they have their place.

"The famous Belgian scholar of the 16th century, Justus Lipsius, used to put on the following show. Lipsius was the editor of the historian Tacitus. He used to stand on a platform and recite Tacitus at request. A man was placed next to him with a naked blade pointed at Lipsius' heart. He was instructed to plunge the blade in if Lipsius should make the slightest misquotation. Well, he lived to put out fine editions of Tacitus and Seneca.

"In ancient tradition, memory was absolutely vital. All the basic texts were memorized and recited from memory: the *Bible*, the *Talmud*, the *Koran*, the *Bhagavad-Gita*. There are various mnemonic devices for helping out: alphabetizations – one sees this in the Psalms where very often the initial letters of the verses form an acrostic on the alphabet – and syllablizations. The whole of the formal Sanskrit grammar is cited and recited from memory and has been cast in a memory-efficient frame.

"At rituals, the chanting was from memory, and in Indian practice, there may be a bank of assistants monitoring the chanting from printed texts as the priests throw the sacrificial rice balls into the fire. If a mistake is made, the ritual may be vitiated. One sees residues of this in synagogue practice. When the Torah is chanted from the Torah Scroll in a special melody, a monitor, standing to the right of the chanter, follows along, and if the monitor is alert and obnoxious, he may pounce upon the chanter if he errs and corrects the errors.

"Every now and then I think it would be great if there were such a thing as a memory pill. One takes such a pill and it enhances the memory for a week or a month. After a month one takes another pill. Then I think that, after all, we are built with more or less just the right amount of memory, and that any increase would have devastating effects. The Battle of the Boyne is remembered in Northern Ireland. The effects have been disastrous. They should forget the Battle of the Boyne. The Battle of Gettysburg should never be reenacted. We also need pills for forgetting. Liquor. Alcohol. Lethe. Anything. Concentrated Lethe."

Upon graduation, Carpenter won the coveted Osborne Travelling Fellowship, and with a couple of letters of introduction from his professors, he found his way to Nepal and to one of the leading monasteries of Mahayana Buddhism. There, in the monastery library, poking around casually, just as you or I might poke around the magazine counter at LaGuardia Airport, he was intrigued by a 14th-century document he found describing the practices of Himalayan shamans. He recognized that some of the practices were similar to magical procedures in Asia Minor many centuries before, and he wondered whether these practices were still around in the Nepalese villages. He arranged for visits, staying in the houses of the headmen. He watched the shamans at work, and listened to what people said. He concluded that the rituals had remarkable stability and had hardly changed in the intervening seven hundred years.

I should assert firmly that Carpenter's reasons for going to Nepal were not, as was the case with so many Americans a decade later, the search for the spiritual enlightenment of Buddhism. Carpenter grew up in the New Hampshire Congregationalism of Saturday night baked bean church suppers, and he combined this, in his own words, with "a fairly devout agnosticism."

To him all religions were equally and marvellously fascinating and equally ridiculous; and all, if the occasion should arise, were equally grist for the mills of his scholarship. To him, all men likewise were equally fascinating and equally ridiculous, and he had the cast of mind that viewed individual differences in the wonderfully ironic light that magnifies these differences into eccentricities. He would have been the first to admit the eccentricity of his own profession, the first to allow the shortcomings of its Great Personalities, and the first to swear eternal fealty to its standards and its traditions.

For all this, Carpenter was not a bigot or a boor, and he would claim that while his own philosophic stance was that of a minimal ironic stoicism and that that stance worked for himself, he did not think it would work for his neighbors and did not advocate it for his children.

Why, then, did Carpenter go to Nepal? Put simply, the driving force of his scholarly pursuits had been to try to understand how knowledge, ideas, tradition, and custom flow back and forth over the ages, from peoples to peoples, nations to nations, from great men to great men, following migratory and nomadic aberrations, following trade, following the paths of conquest. To understand how the ideas of the East and the West combined and merged, were exchanged and were recombined, has been his grand task, the goal that pulled him and the passion that must ultimately be spent.

Like Francis Parkman, a fellow New Englander of the previous century and a historian of the American Indian, the American forest, and the American Empire of France, Carpenter early set for himself a life's program of study and scholarship. The metronome of his inquiry beat steadily for him and it beat not largo, not andante, and at the coda he would have added (he liked to say) a few measures to the restoration of the past and to a new understanding of the integrity of discarded ideas. The libraries of the West are not well supplied with the primary material of the East. At the age of nineteen Carpenter turned to the East for the first time and was to return many times thereafter.

He told me once of a recent East–West exchange that particularly amused him. Astrology is pervasive in most of India today. Horoscopes are cast and opportune dates worked out as a matter of routine. No Indian atomic physicist working in the traditions of modern quantum physics would deny his daughter a wedding whose date had been set by a competent astrologer. The California-based American astrologer Larry the Great was particularly popular in India. His books sold well there and his approach to astrology was very influential.

When I objected that surely this was a case of discredited ideas being rewarmed and served up like last week's beans, Carpenter said he meant this example only as a simple case of the exchange of ideas. This could be important in its own right if, for example, Larry the Great had done computer astrology, and if this had become greatly popular in India, and if this had led to an intensification of computer usage in India and if this intensification had led to the utilization of computers for purposes that were more conventional, technologically speaking. Then Larry and his fellow astrologers would, in this way, have influenced a civilization substantially.

Upon his return to the United States several years later, Carpenter did two things simultaneously. He enrolled as a graduate student in the School for Near Eastern Studies at the University of Chicago, and he announced to the world that he was ready to be married. He told me that he considered the matter of marriage thoroughly. He had examined the lives of A.E. Housman, A.D. Nock, Harry Wolfson, bachelors and scholars all, and concluded that bachelorhood was not for him; that, by and large, the sum of his felicities would be augmented by marriage.

"He makes himself out to be a cold and calculating rationalist," I said one day to Helen Carpenter, his wife.

"He isn't really," she answered me. "This was his excuse when he woke up one morning and found himself married. He likes to say that he thought it through. He didn't. He works on impulsive intuition."

I once asked Helen whether Carpenter was the stereotypical scholar, absent-minded, childlike in innocence, inept at mechanical things, a guy who can't put on two socks of the same color because of the cobwebs of erudition in his brain.

"To some extent. But he works to overcome it. He really does. He thinks that kind of an image doesn't do much for scholarship."

"How does he work on it?"

"By rules of thumb. About ten years ago – I guess it was just after our second girl was born – Alex was leaving for his office and I could see his collar bulging out. I looked closer and found that he had put on two shirts and two ties, one on top of the other. He said to me 'If that's the way things are going to be then I won't wear any ties', and he never has, since that day."

I should point out that the Carpenters had two children, girls, Pro and Doo (Proty and Deutera: Greek for first and second). Pro is married and runs a whole-earth food store on Cape Cod with her husband. Doo is an oboist with one of the midwest symphony orchestras. Neither, as is often the case with children, has had much interest in anything that concerned their parents, particularly their father.

4

Breakfast at the Carpenters'

What was home life like for the Carpenters? From what I saw of it, from what Helen Carpenter told me over the years, and from what Carpenter himself told me, I've put together a little scenario which, if it didn't occur as an actual historical event, might very well have occurred. The components are authentic. In what follows, I shall postulate that it is summer, and I have been an overnight guest at the Carpenters' summer house in Stoddard, New Hampshire, a small village in the southwest part of the state. In the morning, after breakfast, I intend to drive over to the MacDowell Colony and say hello to Lorenzo Kendrick, a writer friend who is in residence at the colony.

It is a glorious day, and the breakfast table has been set out on the deck, which faces south and affords a splendid view of Mount Monadnock. The deep blue clematis twining around the railings are just about to burst.

Carpenter has a slight inclination for what is called a full British breakfast. This is due to the months he's clocked up in England working in the libraries of the British Museum of Oxford and Cambridge Universities and the Warburg Institute. Accordingly, scrambled eggs, toast, canned kippers and mushrooms, leftover cold baked beans, strawberry jam, and coffee have been hauled out from the kitchen. We three take our places.

Carpenter, in excellent spirits, recited a lengthy grace, rather magisterially.

"Oculi omnium in te sperant, Domine, et tu das illis cibum in tempore, aperis manum tuam, et imples omni animal benedictione. Benedic, Domine, nos, et dona tua, quae de tua largitate sumus sumpturi, et concede ut illis salubriter nutriti, tibi debitum obsequium praestare valeamus, per Jesum Christum Dominum nostrum. Amen.

Then – I assume it was for my sake – he rendered it in English:

"The eyes of all wait upon you, Lord, for you have given them food in due season; you open your hand and fill every living thing with blessing. Bless us, Lord, and these your gifts which we are about to receive from your bounty, and grant that, having received healthful nourishment from them, we may be strengthened to lives of grateful service, through Jesus Christ, our Lord. Amen."

A moment of silence followed, after which we three ploughed into the food. I broke the silence.

"I thought you were an agnostic, Alex. Why the grace?"

"I find it irreverent on such exalted occasions as this, when you've honored our table with your presence, to pass it over without a few words thrown in the direction of the transcendental. After all, mankind did not of its own volition bring forth the bread and the jam, let alone the eggs and the kippers."

"But . . . "

"Yes, I suppose my grandfather would have been scandalized by the exact words I recited. But there's a swing to them, and they bring back memories of High Table at Oxford."

Breakfast was the meal Carpenter most enjoyed. I've often thought it was the high point of his material existence. Less complicated than dinner but deeply satisfying, Carpenter was fortified and renewed by breakfast. It was the esse of the esse and the posse of the esse, if I can describe it in a bit of my own Latin. The eggs and kippers seemed to be animated and to say to him: "Let now the day begin. Let now people, events, ideas come as they may."

Carpenter mused this morning that as the earth spins, someone, somewhere must always be sitting down to breakfast.

"You know, the sun never sets on the breakfasters of the world. How marvellous. An instance of Nature's providence. It might have been laid out otherwise."

Helen remarked that she thought that for Canis Minor, their dog, breakfast was also the important meal of the day.

Carpenter agreed. His mind then wandered farther afield.

"What do you suppose the nightingale eats upon waking. . . ."

"Worms and bugs," Helen answered distinctly.

Carpenter did not hear her reply.

73

" . . . and what about the Arctic fox and the little blue herons of the Caribbean?"

Released dimensionally from both time and human personality, Carpenter's mind roved backward and farther afield.

"I wonder what John and Abigail Adams ate for breakfast, or George III, for that matter. It must be recorded somewhere. Do you suppose that Napoleon had croissants and coffee before the Battle of Marengo?"

"Bagels and cream cheese, I should suppose," Helen answered. "They're more substantial."

"What songs the sirens sung or what breakfast Achilles took when he hid among the women, though unknown, are not altogether beyond conjecture."

"Goat cheese and olives," Helen conjectured.

"I suspect you're right," I agreed, cheerily.

Silence for a while, and the sound of crunching toast. Then I spoke up.

"And what about the literary ghosts? The ghost of Hamlet's father, for example. What did he eat for breakfast?"

Helen answered immediately.

"Danish pastry, I'd say. More coffee?" A family argument developed.

"But pastry exists in the world of real alimentation. One must not mix metalevels in cookery."

"I'll mix whatever's required. I'll ask Molly Mowbray. She told me that last fall a ghost came into the Monadnock Inn, said he was the ghost of Franklin Peirce, and ordered a bowl of porridge."

"And I shall consult the authorities on that point, my dear," Carpenter responded gravely. "There are several points of view. That ghosts exist quite beyond the material requirements of the living. The opposite view is that, to the contrary, ghosts live it up in a world awash in the human trash that's been brought forth and been converted into desiderata."

"And the Lamia," Carpenter went on, "The lady demon. What did she have for breakfast? Yes, I know. The blood of the handsome young men she'd seduced. Philostratus says so in Book Four."

Thinking there might be a story in it for me, I pumped Carpenter.

"What does Philostratus say in Book Four?"

"Well, when Apollonius of Tyana was staying in Corinth, he had a student of philosophy named Menippus Lycias. The Lamia set her heart on Menippus. She pretended she was a Phoenician lady living on the outskirts of the city. 'Come this evening. We'll open a bottle of wine the like of which you've never tasted. And I'll sing you a song you would not have thought possible. And, mind, no one will be around so we'll share our beauty between ourselves, if you know what I mean.' That sort of thing."

"Down market behavior. Not very ladylike."

"Rather. But Menippus was taken in. He went to her. And he went again and again. They shared much beauty. Rather nice euphemism, don't you think? And then he promised to marry her."

"He didn't know she was a demon?"

"He didn't, but Apollonius suspected it. Apollonius said he'd come to the wedding. It was held in a grand banquet hall. The place was decorated lavishly with flowers. The meal was catered with waiters serving exotic tidbits on golden trays, cupbearers bearing wine in jewelled cups. Musicians played; delicious perfumes wafted over the vast expanse. The guests marvelled at the magnificence of it all."

"Sounds like an affair that'd cost the bride's family $150 a plate," Helen judged.

"Into this scene, then, strode Apollonius and spoke up."

75

"He would stir things up," Helen put in irreverently. I wondered how many times she heard this story.

" 'Who supplied all this gear, the hall, the dishes, the flunkies? You or the lady?'

" 'The lady did, Apollonius. I'm as true a philosopher as you are. You know that professors own only what's on their back.'

" 'Then I have the honor to say to you that all this before you is unsubstantial. It is a mirage, an illusion. It doesn't exist. The lady is a LAMIA. Can't you see she's fattening you up for her pleasure?' 'Begone foul dream.' Keats.

"The beautiful bride, if you can call her a bride, turned white. She denied the charge. She appealed to the guests. Everyone knows, she said, that philosophers speak a great deal of nonsense."

"And so they do," Helen interpolated. "Most of the time."

"Agreed; well, some of the time surely. Apollonius pressed. The Lamia began to weep. Apollonius pressed harder. He forced a confession out of her. The scene began to disintegrate. The plate disappeared. The trappings. The flunkies. The golden dish wallahs. Finally, the Lamia herself dissolved into a dew. Apollonius and Menippus found themselves alone in the bush at the edge of Corinth."

"Saved by a philosopher?" I teased Carpenter.

"Why not? Of course, the Lamia wasn't a ghost, in the technical sense."

"She wasn't? What was she?"

"She was a succubus. Rather a different kettle of fish. I mean as regards the taxonomy of its non-existence. Isn't it marvellous the way we can classify all kinds of things that don't exist? Hmm. Without irreverence intended, the Almighty Himself has been defined by some medievals as the Negation of all Negations. So existence and non-existence are intertwined. Inextricably. Hmmm. Yes. Ghosts. Now what do ghosts, properly speaking, eat for breakfast?

"Foolish question? Idle curiosity? The best questions are foolish. You know, Frederich II of Sicily, Hauenstauffen, the Stupor Mundi, the Wonder of the World (as regards kings, that is) confronted Michael Scotus with a list of foolish questions. Where is the Great Abyss located and what's beneath it? That sort of thing. If it weren't for all the foolish questions asked, there would be no progress. What came before the Big Bang? The world would be in a situation of stasis."

"Well," I said, responding to all this, "if I'm ever going to get to the MacDowell Colony on time, I'd better interrupt my situation of stasis, delightful as it to be with you here, and pack up."

Breakfasts with the Carpenters, it seems plain enough, had their own metaphysics.

5
Talismans by the Dozen

I popped in on Carpenter one afternoon and found him busy at his microfilm reader. His brown mutt, Canis Minor, now had a grown son, Canis Major. The dogs were both sleeping among the piles of books on the floor.

"What are you doing?"

"I'm preparing a catalog of the holdings of one of the private collections in South India."

"Say – how'd you ever get into this racket of yours in the first place?"

"It was due to my grandfather's grandfather."

"I suppose all our troubles stem from our ancestors."

"Our ancestors shouldn't have been born. 'But how many have that luck? Not one in a hundred,' " he answered, quoting the old joke.

"What did your grandfather's grandfather do?"

"He was a minister in Contoocook. He was also a farmer, of course."

"Was he one of those New England divines who ploughed the ground with the reins in one hand and a Hebrew grammar or a Plato in the other?"

Carpenter answered that it might well have been the case.

"In fact you've put your finger right on the button." He went over to a shelf and took down a volume in Hebrew which he gave me, saying that it had come down in the family from his grandfather's grandfather. He explained that it was a *Hagaddah* – the Passover Table Service – and that it was printed in Leghorn in 1782.

"There are hundreds if not thousands of different editions of the *Hagaddah*. This one is not particularly rare. I found it in a crate in the hayloft of our garage. I must have been eight or nine at the time. The exotic typefaces and the funny medieval pictures interested me."

"How did this strange book come to Contoocook in the 1830's?" I asked him.

"I don't really know how it did. It's easy to make up a plausible story. Jewish peddler came through selling pots, pans, needles, thread. He had this book in his wagon. My ancestor happened to see it. Etcetera. Etcetera. Anyway, it got me thinking. And here I am now doing this index."

★ ★ ★

There should be monuments, there should be odes
to the first flaker of flints
who forgot his dinner
the first collector of sea-shells
to remain celibate.   — *W.H. Auden*

And ditto, I say, for the Carpenters of this world.

The processes of scholarship are carried out in private. The hours of study mount to the thousands and the ten thousands. The head wearies from old documents, illegible and obliterated writing, words whose meanings have been lost for centuries. The eye stings and waters from the oscillating and fuzzy blue light of the microfilm reader. The nose runs long and wet, irritated by the dust of antiquity that rises when the crates of paper, parchment, papyrus, and clay fragments are examined and sorted, matched and patched.

Yet, over the long run, facts are sifted, judged, and reconstructed. Chronologies are rectified and reconciled. The process is painstaking and often dull. But from it, dead words and dead worlds come to life and acquire meaning, and from this dust there emerges a provisional picture of the greatnesses and the follies of the past.

The Victorian novelist George Eliot cruelly satirized and reviled those who engage in this work. We laugh at her picture of Dr. Casaubon in *Middlemarch*, a man who worked endlessly and ineffectually putting the myths of the world together into a unified system. The scholar stands there trivialized. Underlying her parody stands the figure of the great Isaac Casaubon who put the world straight as to the provenance of the *Pimander* and was able to desacralize Hermes Trismegistus, a mighty presence who had occupied a central role in medieval thought.

A Herman Melville or a W.H. Auden may yet arise to celebrate the peculiar driving madness of ancient scholarship and to elevate its Ahabs to mythological status. Let the present story be a tiny step in that direction.

Consider Carpenter. Was it in Carpenter sitting under the lamp that I found the phosphorescence of his learning? Not really. Where was it then? It was in his conversation that he glowed, came alive. His eyes gleamed and sparkled, his nostrils twitched with the excitement of Job's warhorse. Like Ezekiel, he prophesized over dry bones and the bones came together and flesh covered them. He prophesized again, and the living breath invaded them. Carpenter the scholar became Carpenter the storyteller. He was in the tradition of the singers of the Iliad, of the professional narrators who sat in the Suq in Baghdad and for a copper would spin tales the likes of which would make the *Thousand and One Nights* seem pallid.

Not normally talkative, a true son of New Hampshire for whom the simple "Yup" and "Nope" are often considered blabbermouth, Carpenter, under proper circumstances, opened up and poured forth. Carpenter told tales of gods and devils, of arms and the man, but rather more often of scholars, geniuses and eccentrics; of their ideas, their practices and their books. He knew how they felt and how they thought. He got under their skin. He himself metamorphosed as he related his tales, like Apuleius in *The Golden Ass*, and was transformed momentarily into his subject.

Built around the personalities of his profession, his stories were of the library, the museum, the booksellers, the auctioneers, the bibliophiles, the translators, the paleographers, the forgers, the compilers, the editors, the interpreters, the commentators, the collators, the scribes, the epigraphers, the archaeologists, the grave robbers. In short, he sang of all those who had ever dealt with the interpretation and transmittal of the written word. He sang also of their lays, their raw material. The characters in his cast once lived; they are not fiction. That was the difference, the electricity.

There was one problem, however. His transitions in and out of texts, in and out of his personal experience, in and out of his imagination, were so smooth that I could never tell what parts were of his own fabrication. I will say though, that when Carpenter provided me with a reference to a book or to a journal article, and I had occasion to check it out, I never once found the reference to be pure invention.

Start him anywhere. One name, one event rapidly suggested another, and the past was exposed like the webbing of an intricately woven basket. The principal actors were displayed as exercises in landscape architecture, for to Carpenter the mind of each individual was a unique county. He studied the geography of thought. Start him anywhere. His mind would flit, search, and land, and before you knew it, he would dig in at someone you had never heard of, say Elias Ashmole. He would then output stories in mighty quantities.

"Yes Ashmole. Ashmole. A lively character. Very attractive. But a fruitcake. Why did he work so hard writing about the Order of the Garter? Preferment? Something deeper. There was a woman a few years ago, Margaret Murray, who thought that some of the Garter ceremonies were derived from the witches. But that can't be. Could demolish that pretty fast. But we know Ashmole was looking for something deeper than pomp and circumstance. In those days, there was no such thing as empty ceremony. Every ceremony meant something. It's true, of course, that ceremonies degenerate. Ashmole was looking for hermetic significance. Think I can establish that.

"Yes, Ashmole. On July 25, 1678, he wrote in his diary that he

81

placed talismans of rats and moles in the corner of his garden to ward off these pests. He scribbled a few abbreviated technical notes in the margin of his diary: 'At 1 H., P.M., Scorpio ascended. Then hora Saturn Nat. begins. And till 15' after 1 hour of Saturn Art continues. This is the better time, because the natural hour of Saturn when weak is best to dismiss. . . .'

"Here is expiring western astrology drawing its last intellectual breath. Astrology was despised by a few, rejected by many, practiced widely, and in Ashmole's day, it still held on to a tenuous connection with the new science that was emerging.

"Yes, Ashmole. He was Windsor Herald for a while. He was astrologer to Charles II for a while. He advised Charles on what his relations to Parliament ought to be. Via horoscopes, naturally.

"He was one of those magicians who founded the 'Royall Society for the Promotion of Physico-Mathematicall Experimentall Learning.' Yes, think of it, all those Fellows of the Royal Society today got their start from magicians. Have they progressed beyond that?

"When I say magician, I don't mean a prestidigitator, an illusionist who saws pretty ladies in half. I mean an individual who is convinced that by enchantment and spells the world can be compelled to bend its ways to the will and desire of the enchanter. I mean an individual who is convinced that the magical aspects of the cosmos are based upon secret knowledge transmitted to the adept who are capable of understanding, and that this esoteric knowledge goes hand in hand with rational knowledge, and together, they constitute our understanding of the cosmos.

"Shall I tell you how Tommaso Campanella performed the rituals of philosophic magic in the Chambers of Pope Urban VIII? What did he do there? Well, one can only guess really, but it would go along these lines. Here's Campanella's recipe for warding off the evil effects caused by eclipses of the sun or the moon. One goes into a room that can be sealed off against the outside air. One improves the seal by hanging white cloths about. One then lights five torches representing the five planets and two lamps representing the sun and the moon. One arranges for a representation of the twelve signs of the zodiac and distributes about the room stones, plants, and colors that are associated with Jupiter and Venus, the good planets. One arranges for Jovial and Venereal music to be played and, by way of accompaniment, one drinks liqueurs distilled astrologically.

"What is Jovial music? What is Venereal music? How does one distill astrologically? Shall I tell you about the four humours of medieval physiology, the blood, the phlegm, the choler, and the black bile, and their relationship to the five planets?

"Can we not forgive a scholar when he attaches to his refrigerator little notes that say 'Check Aelius Lampridus' *Life of Heliogabalus*' instead of 'Buy bread and tomatoes?'

"Talking about witches, do you know John Evans? No? Fine fellow. I'll tell you. He was in charge of a spirit or an angel named Salmon. He used to employ Salmon to fetch and haul. Mission Impossible sort of thing. He maintained a hot action line. If you needed a hard job done, then you got ahold of John Evans and Salmon. Not cheap but perfectly reliable.

"Evans was an Oxford graduate. A minister, naturally. This was around 1620 or 1630. Somewhere in Staffordshire there was a young lady who married a wealthy old codger. May–December kind of thing. He loved her well enough and wanted to set her up after he had departed from the scene. So he bought a valuable property which he figured would yield her a good income. For some reason (I'd better ask an English solicitor about this. Say, didn't you tell me you had a cousin or something who's a lawyer in London?) he bought the property in the name of a man who was a friend to his wife and who would act as the trustee of her estate.

"The codger died and the young widow went to her so-called friend and said to him, 'hand over the deed.' The friend said 'nothing doing.' Months passed by. Still nothing doing. The young widow was advised to consult the Rev. Evans. Evans said the case was apple pie simple and that would be forty pounds, please, a very substantial sum in those days.

"Evans, being under the dominance of the planet Mars, got in touch with the Angel Salmon. To accomplish this, he read the litany in the *Book of Common Prayer* at certain special times and kept his surplice on all day long. After a week or ten days, Salmon appeared and got his instructions from Evans. The deed of purchase was in a wooden chest in such-and-such a place in the so-called friend's house. After a short while, Salmon reappeared with the deed and placed it on a white tablecloth that Evans had prepared in advance. Then Salmon vanished, presumably called away on other missions. Like the AAA. I should point out that in order to get at the deed, Salmon found it necessary to blow part of the man's house to smithereens. Mafioso techniques on the part of the angelic.

"Now talking about guys who worked with spirits, you surely must have heard of John Dee."

"No. Never heard if him."

"You've not heard of Dee? Where've you been? A fine fellow, Dee. The classic mathematician-astrologer. Crystal ball gazer. His crystal ball is still available at the British Museum. Ask for Freddie Tyng-Ashcroft. He'll show you round all the Deeiana they have. Funny word that. We'll have to invent something better. Let me tell you about Dee. More wine?

"Tyng-Ashcroft was a student of mine the year I taught at Oxford. Useful to have a student in such a key museum slot. Henry Adams said that a friend in office is a friend lost. That's the difference between friends and students. A student is always a student, even if you're eighty and the student's sixty, or you're ninety and the student's seventy. Useful things students. But if they didn't exist, we would not invent them. Repeat: not. Now let me tell you Dee's story, my dear Phil. You are about to be regaled."

Yes, if learning exhibits a phosphorescence, it is a radiation of inner enthusiasm that works its way out of the scholar. If, as in the case of Carpenter, it is his storytelling, then the irony is that the story is often the very least part of the whole scholarly enterprise.

6
John Dee – Nonlinear Version

"Where shall I start? With the crystal ball or with the first English edition of Euclid?"

"Start at the beginning. Go through to the end."

"Nonsense. Impossible. Life is not one damn thing after another. That's for encyclopaedias. Life is ... what? ... a vortex of interlinked contingencies and simultaneities, and even Einstein denies the possibility of simultaneity.

John Dee at middle age

Linearity is an aesthetic possibility not an aesthetic necessity. Euclid's linearity – hypothesis, plunk, plunk, plunk, conclusion – was not the way the facts of geometry were discovered.

"You know when I realized this? When I was a kid and my grandad and grandmother used to sit around the kitchen talking.

She was a great gabber and my grandad would smoke his pipe and put in a grunt every now and then for punctuation. Shall I give you an imitation? She might begin –

" 'The iceman come this afternoon. Brought in a fifty-cent piece. I asked him why he brought in that big a piece. He said his horse had a sore hoof. I said my dad had a horse with a sore hoof and Jimmy White the blacksmith up to Pohawk Mountain said rub it with turpentine. When was that, he said. I said it was around 1910, maybe earlier. The iceman said he didn't remember Jimmy. It was before his day and then he went out the pantry door and the screen didn't shut. Why can't we get a new spring? Even the flies can push that door open.

" 'That Alice Saunders that married Jimmy White, she was a great catch for him as I remember. He had nothing, and spent what he had at Rockingham Race Track. But she reformed him. This was after the kids come. He found Jesus, he did, and that was a blessing.'

" 'Ayuh. How come he brought in a fifty-cent piece?'

" 'He said the ice card in the window was sitting there long side up. And so it was. But I said that was no answer as he knew my ladies' group always comes on Thursday afternoons and I needed the space on top of the ice to put my big bowl of whipped cream. He said well, Mrs. Carpenter, your card was up the long way and I'm not going to take the ice out and shave it down, 'cause the horse has a sore hoof and don't want standing around. Said I could put the ice on the top of the stove and melt it down if my bowl didn't fit. Fresh fellow today, I'm thinking.'

" 'Ayup'.

"Linearity? No way. With a linear policy, my grandmother would have run out of material in one minute flat.

"Well, Dee. John Dee. Capital fellow. Mathematician. Alchemist.

Virtuoso on the chrystal ball. CIA agent for Queen Elizabeth the First. That was the rumor anyway. Of course Elizabeth had an intelligence network set up for her by Walsingham. Very important. Mary of Scotland was trying to dethrone her. If Dee worked for Walsingham, then Walsingham didn't do much for him financially or by way of preferment. But then the Queen didn't do much for Walsingham either.

"Actually, Elizabeth liked Dee and every once in a while she'd come up the river and stop off at his place at Mortlake and take a look at his laboratory. He'd be out in the back cooking and pounding and distilling, trying to make cheap gold – that would show the Spaniards – and the Queen would come by. So he'd stop and set up his large parabolic mirrors that invert the image. The Queen was amused, and she'd leave him a small purse or a dozen brace of grouse and then move on.

"Actually, Dee had an excellent education. Cambridge. Read Greek. He was one of the original Fellows of Trinity. Then he worked on mathematics and astronomy. He was associated with the first English language edition of Euclid. He could have had a job as Reader in Mathematics at the University of Paris. He had lectured there on Euclid to standing room only, and was offered the job. But he was moving from mathematics and astronomy to astrology and alchemy. It was the critical decision of his life. He turned down the Paris job. What a mistake. He probably would have made a first rate mathematician if he'd stuck with it.

"He was chief scientist of the realm, if there had been such a title. In this capacity, when Mary Tudor became Queen of England, he was asked to prepare a horoscope for her. Not long after, he was arrested on a charge of sorcery and was brought to the Star Chamber for trial. He was acquitted, but the suspicion of witchcraft clung to him throughout his life.

"Do you know that when Dee was an old man he petitioned King James I that he be tried for witchcraft, and if found guilty that he be put to death? He wanted to clear his name of the chronic suspicion. James ignored the petition. Quite right, too.

"When Dee was chief scientist, so to speak, the Earl of Leicester called him in and asked him to determine an auspicious date for the coronation of the young Queen Elizabeth. What a marvellous job Dee did. What scientific advisor to a head of state has ever done a better job? He had a vision of England as a great sea power and he was the first man to use the expression 'The British Empire.' He formulated plans for setting up a great national library.

"Nothing came of the library for two hundred years. For shame. He was asked to review the calendar reform of Pope Gregory. He found that the astronomy was sound. He told Elizabeth as much. She turned down the suggestion. Protestant-Catholic politics, you know. The Pope was right, of course. England finally made the correction in 1752.

"Dee was p.o.'d and sought consolation and advice from the spirits that lived in his crystal ball. On the whole, as I've said, Elizabeth liked Dee and would have advanced him. The persistent rumors of sorcery prevented her. Talking about calendar reform, I could make a list as long as my sleeve of all the times that religion has prevented scientific truth from surfacing. The reverse question is also interesting: how often does science prevent other truths than its own from being heard? Would you believe it, the positivists think that scientific truth is the only possible kind of truth? 'What is truth?' asked jesting Pilate, but would not stay for an answer.

"But back to the crystal balls! Are you ready? The thing you have to realize about crystal gazing is that it's a two-man job. You don't do it by yourself. One man is a medium or a skryer. The skryer looks in the ball and, if he's a receptive medium, he sees things in it. He then reports what he sees – not always comprehensibly – to the second man who has to interpret the visions and implement them.

"Dee experimented with skryer after skryer. Dee was a scientist, or a pre-scientist working along unprofitable lines. It happens every day of the week, even today. Mystic documents and occult writings poured from Dee's pen as a result. They're all in the British Museum now. Talk to my student Tyng-Ashcroft. Finally, Dee found a guy by the name of Edward Kelley, whom, after a trial period, he came to regard as the perfect medium. Actually, Kelley was a rascal, an unscrupulous adventurer, but an interesting guy.

"At this point in his life Dee's financial position was very bad. Lab equipment cost a lot of money. Dee was in and out of debt. No money forthcoming from the Crown, Dee succumbed to a proposition offered him by Albert Laski, who was Count Palatine of Siradia, some tiny place in central Europe, to come to his place and make gold. What if he had succeeded? Cheap gold? Did they know any economics in those days? Did you know that after the Spaniards got their hands on all that gold in Mexico and South America, there was terrific inflation in Europe?

"Laski turned out to be a pauper among princelings, and Dee latched on to another somewhat wealthier prince, Count William Rosenberg, Viceroy of Bohemia and Knight of the Golden Fleece. Rosenberg installed Dee, his wife and family, and Kelley and his wife (Kelley had no children) in his castle in Bohemia. Near Prague. Dee's job: to make gold. This was during the reign of Rudolf II, of the Holy Roman Empire. A great emperor, but neurotic like a fruitcake. No, take that back, manic-depressive. But Rudolf assembled a brilliant collection of scientists, artists: Tycho Brahe, Kepler, Arcimboldo.

"The experimentation continued. There were magic powders.

A philosopher's stone was set up. There was more crystal gazing and angelic visions. The prospect of synthetic gold was just around the corner.

"Now Kelley was unhappy. He would have liked to set up in the alchemy business on his own, independently of Dee. The relationship between the two men deteriorated. Kelley was on the outs with his own wife. He never really liked her in the first place and he reproached her for not bearing him a child.

"The crystal gazing continued. Voices told Kelley why he had no children: he'd picked the wrong mate. He let Dee in on a vision he'd had. A female angel by the name of Madimi informed Kelley that the Dees and the Kelleys must share and share alike, in all things. To underline her point, the angel Madimi did a strip tease in the crystal ball. Well, that's what we'd call it now. Kelley, so he said, did not understand the message. He was only the skryer, not the interpreter. Eventually the message came through loud and clear: swap wives. Dee heard the message, but could not see Madimi.

"This celestial directive led to general consternation in the little ménage. Kelley pretended innocence: he was only the medium. Dee was grief-stricken. How could pure angels propose such an arrangement that contradicted God's Laws? Jane Dee was informed. She was shocked and furious. So was Kelley's wife. A rerun was demanded by the two wives. Upon the rerun of the procedure, the angel Raphael put in his two cents' worth. After this independent consultation with Raphael, Dee drew up a document, a four-way covenant, a pious instrument of mystical, philosophical wife-sharing, to be carried out in a spirit of friendship, without lust, and for the purposes of furthering human knowledge and spiritual values.

"After the document was signed, Dee continued to drag his

feet. He was a devout Christian. Weeks passed. Finally Dee went into the castle chapel and spread the covenant on the altar and prayed for guidance. His heart was strengthened. The worst was now over. Kelley gave up and quit the premises in a tantrum. The partnership was terminated.

"It delights me to tell you that Kelley came to a bad end. And that's it."

"That's it?"

"That's it, essentially. Of course we have crates of information. It's in the British Museum. A good deal of it is undeciphered."

"Does the first edition of Euclid come in at all?"

"Well, it doesn't play a role in the crystal gazing stuff. It was part of Dee's accomplishments as a bona fide scientist in the currently established sense. In 1570 a man by the name of Henry Billingsly, who was later Lord Mayor of London, edited and published the first English edition of Euclid. Dee contributed a long introduction to this book – in fact, some people think he did the whole book, but I have a hunch he didn't. At the time Dee wrote the introduction, he was already under suspicion of sorcery. The main reason for the suspicion seems to have been that Dee collected or constructed many wonderful mechanisms. Today we would call them wind-up toys.

"Dee's introduction to Euclid has hardly anything to do with geometry as such. It's a remarkable defense of science as a whole and of himself in particular against the charge of sorcery. He talked about many wonderful mechanisms that he'd seen or heard about that, at first glance, might appear to be the works of the Devil but, in reality, were based upon perfectly natural principles. In my view, it's one of the most remarkable introductions ever to appear in a mathematics book.

"Look at it in today's context. Atomic energy, genetic engineering, computers. Natural principles? Works of the Devil? Both?"

7
Carpenter to the Rescue

Carpenter despised politics and politicians. He rarely voted in national elections. His attitude, I used to think, was paradoxical. On the one hand, there was no logical reason preventing world affairs from being run the way they were run in Contoocook, New Hampshire, when he was a boy: fairly decently but with a small amount of hanky panky to oil the spots where the joints of human relationships don't meet exactly. On the other hand, aware as he was of the flow of thousands of years of history, he denied larger meaning to the whole process, political or social. While he himself would have preferred to live in an environment of town meeting democracy, he asserted that such an arrangement was probably ephemeral, and that all kinds of regimes, from the mildest to the grossest, from the most liberal to the most repressive, had yielded much that was of interest to him. Nor did politics seem to him to be a place where intelligence played a significant role.

As with everything, he would assert that there was no larger meaning to things, and then start to explain to you how the Gnostics uncovered the secret meanings.

Carpenter was a snob, and of a peculiar sort. Not a political snob; as I've suggested, he would at one moment assert the virtues of democracy and at another moment those of autocracy or theocracy. Though his ancestors came over to the shores of New England on the Arbella, he was not a social snob. He asserted that subsequent ships brought over people with ideas that were of equal interest to him, and that the native Indians themselves had their own kayak Arbellas that bridged the continental gap from Asia to Alaska. He was one-eighth American Indian, he said, and one eighth-Italian.

He was not an economic snob; he saw great wealth as one of the strange, unaccountable things that people piled up, some by accident, some by intent. He saw poverty as constantly with us and constantly shifting its definition. He was not an intellectual snob – well, not exactly – he enjoyed a talk with the professors in the Academy as well as with the villager who pumped gas in Contoocook. "From those to whom much has been given," he was fond of quoting, "much will be expected."

He was a snob as regards the right kind of scholarship to be pursued. He regarded my relationship to him pretty much as that of Watson to Sherlock Holmes. I found that when I recorded what he told me, I missed everything that was important to him in favor of what was romanticized and sensational.

He was a snob in that he had absolute confidence in the superiority of his professional work – what he wanted to do and how he proposed doing it. His personal life seemed to me to be subsidiary to his professional life, and he would not allow a deviation by so much as a jot or a tittle from the goals of the latter. Nonetheless, as far as the outside world could tell, his personal life was satisfactory and placid.

I said to Carpenter one day that he ought to gather his vast learning into a system so as to pull it all together. He snapped back at me and, paralleling the words of the great Samuel Johnson, said that if he waited until he had formulated a system, the world would see very little from his pen.

Most of us at some point in our professional lives have stopped and, in a moment of self-examination, wondered whether it was all worthwhile. With Carpenter, it was a bit different: it was all worth nothing to him and it was all worth everything to him, simultaneously.

He was not afraid of his own often heterodox opinions. In a decade that saw the publication of Freudian interpretations of satanism and possession from the pen of Aldous Huxley (*The Devils of Loudun*), the political interpretation of the Salem witch trials from the pen of Arthur Miller (*The Crucible*), and economic interpretations of the same events, Carpenter, who was the direct descendant of two hanged witches, one in Salem, and one in Andover, told me one day that the tradition in his family was that these ancestors felt that they *were* witches.

"Whether or not they were witches is one question. Whether they felt themselves to be witches is another question. And the distinction between the two has never been squarely faced since before Hawthorne's day."

Did Carpenter have any vices? I asked him this one day.

"Vices? Certainly. A man without vices is incomplete. A man without vices is a threat to the angels. More than that, he is a magnet for all the malevolent forces in the world." But Carpenter would not say what his own vices were.

In my own view – personal of course – his book collecting amounted to a vice. He would go without bread – not that he had to – to buy the books he set his heart on. You understand that he was not interested in buying first editions of *Gone with the Wind*. What he wanted, for example, is that rare 1478 copy of Dioscorides Pedanius' *De Materia Medica*. Once the dealers got word that Carpenter was interested in a certain item, and it made no difference whether their shop was in New York, Rome, or Aleppo, the price went up.

To counteract this, Carpenter employed countervailing "devices" which he said I would not understand. This was his way of telling me that he preferred to keep them to himself.

"They are thieves and scoundrels, these dealers. Really. But fine fellows. They're entitled to a living. We get along."

Carpenter was not dishonest.

"It's a game, and we're all in it together. There are very few players and, we're all consenting adults. We set our own rules and play close to the line. What we do in the collecting game is of negligible interest to the rest of humanity. Anyone in the game who made an appeal to the secular authorities would soon find himself without a net and without a racket. I mean no witticism here."

I asked Carpenter whether the supply of ancient books available to collectors and scholars was constant or shrinking.

"One would think, naturally, that since in time everything decays, the supply would diminish. But from my point of view as a collector, things are otherwise. Books get deaccessioned from libraries, great estates are sold and put up for auction. And then, there is one thing that makes it all very interesting: old books are constantly manufactured anew, provided with credentials, and sold on the open market."

"Facsimile editions, I suppose?"

"No. The real thing. Or at least the claim is put out that they're the real thing. And the claim is not always easy to refute. Battle of wits."

I expressed incredulity.

"Some day, when we have a bit of time over lunch, I'll tell you some lovely stories about this."

You could say that one element that was missing from Carpenter's psychological makeup was the poetic. His knowledge was vast, he did his work thoroughly and he drew his conclusions in copious amounts, but he hardly moved beyond what could be concluded from a close reading of the best available texts and the best available interpretation of those texts.

I teased him a bit on this point.

"You say that the establishing of the text and the interpretation of the text may be a two-tier, two-person job?" I asked him one day.

"That's the way it is."

"Isn't that parallel to the chrystal ball gazer and the interpreter?"

"Just shows, doesn't it, that the old boys had the right methods and the wrong metaphysics of the world."

Carpenter's scholarship was conservative: he made no flying leaps into strong conjecture or personal fantasy, nor did he assemble his conclusions into grandiose metaphysical or metahistorical schemes. He was not, as Robert Bridges was, a builder of myths about myths.

Carpenter despised professional philosophy. In my view, if there was a weak spot in his professional makeup this was where it was. He, on the contrary, would have considered it a strength. Oh, rather more than the average college lecturer on the subject, he knew what the ancient and medieval philosophers said, but he claimed no deep scholarship in this region. Current philosophies of art and literature, of history, social philosophies of all kinds, and philosophies of science he regarded as so much trash.

"Philosophy was a Greek toy. It's a noxious spin-off from mathematics and the notion of mathematical proof. Proof was the greatest and everlasting Greek contribution to mathematics. Pythagoras in the fifth century B.C. discovered the square root of two was not an integer and not a fraction. Yet the square root of two is the diagonal of a square whose side has length one. Therefore the square root of two both exists and cannot exist. In an effort to explain this dilemma, the Greeks invented philosophy. A great mistake. One can never explain what is; one only needs to explain what isn't. Ultimately, the dilemma was cleared up not by philosophy but by more mathematics."

I responded that this was close to Karl Popper's philosophy of scientific explanation. Carpenter shrugged aside the name of this distinguished contemporary. He had never heard of him, but countered that the sentiment went all the way back to Isander of Cos, if not before.

No, philosophy was not where Carpenter was. He resided in a world of legend, myth, pagan and primitive religions, ritual, law. He flourished in a universe of thaumaturgy, alchemy, astrology, hermeticism, primitive science, custom, literature, documents. Art, design, and music were weaker for him. He was willing to leave the dating of pottery or ancient jewelry to the shard experts. Stratigraphy was not for him. But as a papyrologist, as a paleographer, he had few peers. The word was the thing. When it was a matter of the word, written, printed, spoken, he came alive.

In 1980 I spent a semester in Salt Lake City teaching higher mathematics at the University of Utah. I sublet a convenient apartment, and I was joined by my wife only occasionally as she had other fish to fry back home. In my isolation, I wrote to Carpenter asking him to rescue me by suggesting some amusing bedtime reading. There ensued a short correspondence in which he obliged me with a list of what he called "ancient weirdos" and suggested that I begin with the *Acta Sanctorum*, "a many-volumed and marvellous repertory of strange lives."

I found the *Acta* in the Marriott Library of the university, and wrote to him that I had selected a volume at random and had dug in. Carpenter immediately responded with more suggestions. I reproduce his letter here as a fine example of his epistolary style:

6 March 1980

Dear Phil:

I am delighted that the Latter-Day Saints are interested in their predecessors, at least to the extent of having that storehouse of human folly, the *Acta Sanctorum*.

But really, for high amusement, you should try to get hold of a translation (I know that at least there's a French one) of Aelius Lampridius' *Life of Heliogabalus* in the *Historia Augusta*. It starts charmingly:

"I would never have committed the life of Heliogabalus Antoninus (who was also called Varus) to writing in fear that someone might learn he was an Emperor of the Romans if that same Empire had not previously had Caligulas and Neros and Vitelliuses. . . ."

He then proceeds to the details of Heliogabalus' dubious conception (the name Varus is said to have been given to him in honor of the variety of his potential paters). But Heliogabalus was not only noted for his perversity (a memory of which is found in a horoscope published in P Oxy 46 – no. 3298; cf. also 3299), but for his clothes, his furniture, his botanical and zoological collections, and his patronage of actors, barbers, artisans, astrologers, and musicians. I suggest and recommend him particularly because he is one of the few authenticated cases I know of someone who sincerely (?) worshipped himself. An Indian embassy was also sent to greet him on his election to the imperium. The embassy instructed Bar Daisan in Indian symbolism, whose account, as retold by Porphyry, is preserved in the learned Stobaeus.

I assume you have read as well as Philostratus' *Life* and Apollonius of Tyana's own *Letters*, the attack on the latter (or rather on both) by Eusebius. Besides these you must read the account of Apollonius' magical acts in Greek and Arabic given by P. Kraus in vol. 2 (pp. 270 sqq.) of his *Jabir ibn Hayyan*. Jabir (or ps.-Jabir), incidentally, should join our list of wierdos.

Go to al-Biruni. The extraordinary nature of al-Biruni can only come across through reading his many books. For starters, one may turn to his *Chronology* and his *India*, both translated by E.C. Sachau. The translator's preface to the second book, though somewhat inflated in its estimate of the man, is also good. A book that will amuse you (written by a contemporary, and undoubtedly an acquaintance of al-Biruni) is al-Tha'alibi's *Lata'if al-ma'arif*, translated by C.E. Bosworth. Therein you will learn that just four Muslims have begotten each a hundred children, and four have killed each a million men; these facts and other statistics await you.

The microfilm reader awaits me.

Sincerely,
Alex

With all his lists, documentations, and searches for interconnections, why should Carpenter not be considered simply a dry-as-dust scholar, a pedant, a man who pursued the trivial on a higher level? It was simply this, and I've suggested it already. There was Carpenter the scholar and Carpenter the raconteur relating the products of his scholarship. His sense of each event and of its uniqueness, of personality, and his narrative skills were all remarkable. He was an ancient bard reincarnated on the Commons of New England. He stood in the sandals of Homer and when he held forth, one listened in silent amazement. Later, when his story was over, one wondered how could it be that we have allowed the strength of direct oral communication to be so diluted by successive waves of advancing technology.

8
Carpenter and the New Age

In the first years after I met Carpenter, I used think that his scholarly interest in ritual magic was his own personal eccentricity.

After all, according to the wisdom of a positivistic age, magic was intellectually discredited and its study, accordingly, devalued. His fellow scholars in the history of scientific ideas took no such route; they separated out and explicated the works of the great scientists of the deep past whose thoughts led directly to our present vision of science: Archimedes, Diocles, Apollonius, Ptolemy. Or Copernicus, Kepler, Galileo, Newton, Gauss, Euler, Riemann, and Einstein, to name a few non-classical names.

The study of devalued material cannot, of necessity, be of the same value as that which is now considered established. Despite what must have been considerable regret that the history of discarded sciences cannot have the same punch as the history of successful sciences, Carpenter worked in his chosen field steadily, with good humor, and with zest. He always maintained the highest standards of scholarship and exhibited little concern for the opinions and prejudices of what might be called the professional main-liners. Because of these prejudices, Carpenter had his chosen field pretty much to himself. There were a few others, of course, some scholars in Austria, Italy, or Japan who did his sort of thing, and he himself, over the years, had trained a number of younger people. But they, in order to obtain academic positions, had to exhibit familiarity with more conventional matters.

As the years passed and I saw what was transpiring in the larger world, I relaxed my mainstream opinions a bit. While granting to Carpenter the unique talents and interests that he assuredly had, I saw his studies less as a matter of his own idiosyncrasies and more as a part of a contribution to an increasing stream of anti-rational thought and practice that had welled up since the end of World War II.

The war itself creating vast holocausts firmly lodged in modern physics and chemistry (not that Genghis Khan didn't slaughter millions with ancient technology), the cold war and the atomic threat, the pollution of the world through what most of us would have regarded as benign technology, the reduction by medical technology of the human body to a set of replaceable, interchangeable parts, the separation of sex from procreation, and later, of procreation from sex, had all brought into serious question the scientific and technological spirit, and if science had been derived from pure reason, then reason itself was open to question.

As against this, the potential of science for bringing forth new forms, new ideas, new products, and new jobs seemed unlimited. The potential hardly needed the excuse of Cold War defense activity to realize itself, though this helped greatly, and most scientists took the money (and the prestige) and ran without further thought. When they looked beyond everyday triviality, it was as though they stood at the top of the Mountain of Knowledge and saw the possibility of remaking the world. Their knowledge would eliminate hunger and ignorance, relegate all social difficulties and old religious expressions to irrelevance, and bring to the world new social forms. The prospects held forth by science was breathtaking.

With the disillusionment and the collapse of one idealism after another, of social entities, of the family, of "artificial" aggregations of ethnicities, came the counter-culture. Music changed, literature changed, as well as styles of dress, food, manners, and language, the relation of the sexes changed. Mysticisms of numerous forms grew in strength and provided answers to the perennial questions of human life, questions to which positivistic science could only respond with silence.

Opportunistic astrologers, largely ignorant of the astronomical algorithms that formed the basis of historic astrology (what difference would it make, anyway?) plied their trade, often computerized, in the newspapers, on TV, and via telephonic arrangements.

Women discovered, or rediscovered, that they were witches, and practiced rituals aimed at coercing the world. Charismatic gurus sprang up. False messiahs, both religious and medical, flourished, piled up personal fortunes and occasionally led their followers, like lemmings, over the cliff. Zealots, claiming a mandate from the bowels of their personal deities, introduced widespread terrorism, practiced assassination, and preferred death to compromise.

Intellectuals such as Aldous Huxley, a man who was nursed in the scientific tradition, took early to mysticism and promoted the Perennial Philosophy. Men and women were born again into all the classic faiths, which, in turn, were often found again to be empty at best and inhuman at worst. The fundamentalist impulse of all religious denominations waxed powerful, and the authorship of the basic historical religious texts were reassigned to God. Judaism rediscovered its own Chassidic traditions as a rich source of warmth, literature and liturgy, and with the early (1938) and tremendously influential work of Gershom Scholem reinstated the Kaballah as a respectable intellectual discipline.

Knowledge was sought in the writings and the authority of the past, even though such material had been devalued and mocked in recent centuries. Seen against the Renaissance of the Irrational, Carpenter's studies of Eastern science and magic could be viewed not as fortuitous and idiosyncratic, but rather as a logical activity or expression, fitting in with the age, of a man who was a scholar's scholar.

He knew the spells of ancient Egypt, the formulas preserved in the *Pimander*, and the Orphic poetry that must be recited to counteract the maleficent comets. He knew the rituals of Buddhism, Hinduism, and of the Nestorians. He understood what it meant to cast a horoscope, and how to apply geomancy, hydromancy, and the hundred other "-ancies" and "-ologies" that placate the heart of the tormented individual in a world of ambiguities.

I once asked Carpenter whether he knew of a spell which when spoken would annihilate the whole cosmos and all it contained, both physical and mental, and all memory of the same, absolutely and utterly for now and all time. And I recall vividly how he looked up from the book he was reading and said, "I suppose things are not going well with you this afternoon. But since you ask, the Lamaistic monks say such a spell constantly. But it seems not to have kicked in as yet. Here we are! We Westerners are an impatient crew."

Carpenter was learned in alchemy, ancient medicine, hermetic geometry, the secrets of the Rosicrucians. He knew the names of the Ten Thousand Devils of Tantric Buddhism and of the thousand angels of the *Sefer ha Rezin*. He could tell you the messages of the mandalas and the history of the tarot. He knew why a certain sect of Chassidim thought that the latest outrage on the West Bank was due to a vast physical neglect of the mezuzzoth on the doorposts of an Israeli prime minister.

As well as any man who has tried to recover them from the debris of the Roman Empire, Carpenter knew the secret rites of Isis worship and of Mithra. He read the record of the followers of Baal, and he understood, perhaps better than they, what is in the minds of the latter-day Temple worshippers in Israel who seek to restore the Sacrificial Order.

All these things Carpenter knew, and they constituted the raw material out of which he shaped his scholarly mission which was to trace the spread of ideas from land to land.

Thinking of the rising popular demand for occult material and experiences, I said to Carpenter one day that it would be nothing at all for him to become the Prince of the Astrologers, as it were, the

Chief Magician to the New Age. All he would have to do would be to write up in popular form a tiny fraction of what he knew and he would rake in a bundle.

"It is all dreck," he answered me, "all of it. Fascinating, boring, human dreck. Dreck is dreck, but the study of dreck can be scholarship. It can demonstrate how out of what is erroneous can come what is correct. But I won't lend my scholarship to the purposes you've mentioned. If someone wants to put something together on the basis of my writings, well, I can't prevent that. They're out there in the public domain. Go ahead, do it if you want."

Admitting that rationality as the dominating intellectual expression of the age seems to be coming to an end, Carpenter's views on what will follow in the years to come, while not startling, may be of some interest.

"The search for so-called rational action as exhibited through mathematics, computerization, social and physical modeling will continue vigorously. So also will the trend toward mystic philosophies and eschatologies. They will reside side by side in the same institutions and often in the same individuals, regulating different parts of their lives. The universities will teach the latest science and mathematics, and they will also teach a wide variety of religious manifestations, philosophies, rituals, and mysteries.

"There will be some interaction between the two, each drawing on the other, for it's a mistake to think that science derives from pure reason combined with experiment. But whether the two will forge a genuine synthesis is hard to say.

"As far as the quality of our life is concerned, as technology intensifies and provides us with more and more, it will become increasingly manifest that technology is often brutal from the point of view of society. General intelligence will diminish and be replaced by a synthetic intelligence, and a mathematical-like reality will be imposed on the world. Not mandated – mind you – but by acquiescence and a kind of adaptive process.

"By and large, the meaning of life will be provided by the irrational or transcendental elements – this has always been the case – but the form of life will be limited to the patterns allowed by mathematics and physics. The famous reply of Diogenes the cynic to Alexander the Great, 'Get out of my sunshine,' will be reiterated often and with great pathos by those who want to detach but find it impossible to do so.

"Do you want to hear more? Read science fiction. I despise the stuff, but the general outlines are all there. Nature, you know, is said to imitate art. The truth is that much of what is called nature is really man-made. Anyway, I much prefer to study the past than to think about the future. Really, prediction is impossible. If there is one thing I know with any firmness, it's that it's impossible to see very far ahead. How can one know the future when the present is uninterpretable? We only do what we can along those lines."

I took Carpenter up on the question of prediction.

"Isn't there a bit of a paradox involved here? Every scientific system must contain an element of prediction. Civilization relies on prediction. We need to know what will be. And many of our predictive schemes are successful. We can, after all, predict sunrise and sunset with incredible accuracy."

Carpenter's response brought in another aspect of his philosophy which in fact existed, but which he refused to admit or professionalize.

"That's because you're looking over a time interval that's very short, and at events that stand in relative isolation from the larger motions of the cosmos. It's not impossible that a wandering asteroid could collide with the earth tomorrow and knock it off orbit. Where, then, are your predictions?

"So time is involved, and so is probability. There may be an unlimited number of time scales operating independently and correlated with the degree of success in a particular predictive theory.

"A lack of prediction would be the equivalent of destroying time."

9
The Sun and Moon Conjoined

Sometime in a summer of the late sixties, a few years before I had met him, Carpenter made the front page of the *New York Times*, under the heading "Scholar Vanishes in Himalayas." The article went on to say that Alexander Carpenter, a historian and orientalist, while on a research trip to the mountainous regions north of India, had mysteriously vanished. Various conjectures were put forward, of which the most plausible (to the writer at the news service) was that Carpenter was an agent of the CIA, his research trip was really a cover, and he had been kidnapped and was being held hostage.

Messages went back and forth between Washington and Delhi, Delhi and Katmandu. Consuls were alerted, statements were put out: confirmations, denials, hedgings.

After six weeks or so, Carpenter reappeared. He told reporters that on a trip to the remote Golden Monastery of Bulguristan he had become incommunicado because of a major landslide that made the primitive mountain roads and bridges impassable. He also stated that his trip to the Monastery had been a great success, yielding a wealth of documents (including one that he thought might be in the lost Cappadocian language) that had been known to him only by allusions in more familiar material. The tone of the newspaper report was one of mild disbelief, not of the Cappadocian, but of the implied denial of the claim of a CIA connection.

I had myself not known about this episode. Carpenter told me about it one day at a long lunch.

"Has sufficient time now passed that you can tell me the true story of your disappearance?"

"I think so. What I told the reporters when I got back to the States was not entirely false. There had been a landslide and a disruption of communication and travel. But this was repaired after about two weeks. It was also true that I had been kidnapped, so to speak, or at least I'd been detained against my will. And the reason for it had nothing to do with Cold War politics, spies, local revolutions, terrorism, that sort of thing. The reason lay in an ancient ritual, and I found myself, quite by accident, a central figure in this ritual. A nice example of applied mathematics, incidentally."

"Why did you go to Madoof in Bulghuristan in the first place?"

"An interesting story, that. I'll give you the short version. I got carried away by the writings of Abu Ma'shar al-Balkhi (from Balkh, in Bactria, 786–886). Ma'shar was interested in the Hurrians. Biblically, Harran, where Abraham came from. In Harran, the cult of the Moon God Sin was practiced at the Temple of Sin. Incidentally, the Roman Emperor Elagabalus worshipped the Moon God.

"There were many temples in Harran. They practiced lots of astral magic and the temples they built facilitated that. But also, a temple to the divine *Nous*. The Divine Reason. Nice, no? Where, today, are there temples to reason, divine or otherwise? The universities? Hah!

"The Hurrians were the oddballs of the region, isolated from the nearby groups. We know that in the year 830, there was a formal meeting between the Caliph and a delegation of the Hurrians.

"The Caliph asked: 'Are you guys pagans?'

"The Hurrians replied: 'No. We are People of the Book. And we are followers of the Prophet.'

"The Caliph: 'What book?'

"The Hurrians: 'The writings of Asclepius.' (Apollo's son, the god of medicine.)

"The Caliph: 'What prophet?'

"The Hurrians: 'Hermes Trismegistus.'

"As far as I know, there haven't been any proper excavations of Harran. In the 1950's Rice did some digging there. Then he committed suicide. Sad. So we have to rely on medieval Arabic descriptions of the temples. Al-Damashki gave a description of the temples of Harran. But he has precious little to say. Built along strongly geometric lines: octagons, dodecagons, icosagons. Each type keyed to a special planet; more applied mathematics for you. Each built out of special materials also keyed to the individual planets. For example, Saturn was lead or black stone.

"At any rate, I got wind of the fact that around 850 Abu Ma'ashar wrote a book, now lost, on the temples of Harran. The book, I call it the *Book of Temples*, contained, so it was suggested, descriptions of the temples, the temple rituals, and the Hurrian theory of magic. We also have allusions to a later version in Arabic, around 1401, that even contained some drawings of the temples. What a find that would be, if the book could be recovered! And then, in this connection, I ran across an allusion to the area of Bulghuristan."

"And off you went, lickety split, to look in a primitive country for a copy of an ancient book whose existence was, at best, conjectural?"

"Yes, off I went. When one looks, one always finds something of interest, even if it isn't what one expects. Motivation is what counts. I took the bus from Constantinople to Kabul. From Kabul to Faizabad in Badakhstan by jeep. And from Faizabad to Madoof in Bulghuristan by donkey.

"'Hello,' I said in a restaurant-cum-gambling parlor, 'I need a room. I am a scholar and am looking to buy old books.' I said it out loud, so all would hear. That's a good way to advertise in Bulghuristan. A room was offered to me. That's the way the booking system works there.

"After three days I was asked by a delegation consisting of a military man and a priest of the Bulguhri religion would I please come to the Royal Palace for questioning. Not the Police Station, mind you. I was grilled thorough and through. Apparently I gave all the right answers. I was given the Honor of the Sun. But noblesse oblige, don't you know, for at the same time I was informed that I would be held essentially incommunicado in the Royal Palace for about a month.

"I'll now explain to you the basis of my house arrest. The sun and the moon, individually and in combination, were powerful figures – gods – in the minds of the ancients. The joining of the sun and the moon, occurring astronomically when there is an eclipse of the sun, is a theme that runs through ancient mythology and religion. The moon = love = soma = hallucinogenic drugs. How's that for an equation?

"You find the sun–moon theme nicely expressed, for example, in the *Kumarasambhava* of the poet Kalidasa (c. 400). The story of Siva and Parvati."

"Tell me. I don't know it."

"Siva was married to Sati, the daughter of Daksa. There was an exchange of insults between Siva and Daksa. Sati, in despair, practiced asceticism, and so successfully that her body wasted away and disappeared. Her soul (atman) was reborn as Parvati, the daughter of the Mountain (Himalaya). Meanwhile Siva, sorrowing over the loss of Sati, abandoned the world and practiced yoga and entered deep contemplation (samadhi).

"A certain evil fellow by the name of Taraka had been practicing yoga, and he had gained sufficient 'heat' (tappas) that he was able to blackmail Brahma. He threatened to burn the universe, and the price he asked was to be installed in heaven in control of the gods of the rest of creation. The gods were told by Brahma that they could get rid of Taraka only by finding a young leader (Kumara) who will be the son of Siva and Parvati. The gods send Kama, the god of love, to cause Siva to fall in love with Parvati. Siva (the Sun), in his ascetic mode, burns up Kama with the fire from his third eye. But Parvati (the Moon) has, on her own, decided to marry Siva, and she practices asceticism to gain her end.

"While as Sati her asceticism had destroyed her body, as Parvati, it awakens Siva from his asceticism. They are duly married and Kumara is born. End of this story. Would you like to hear a more recent story where the sun and moon get married?"

I had no classes to teach or appointments that afternoon so I said, "Of course, the more stories the merrier."

"Well, this will be quite merry. Have you heard of Elagabulus?"

"Just barely. Who is he?"

"No? You haven't heard? Then you've been missing a treat. Ah yes, Elagabalus. Also known as Heliogabalus. Also known as Varius Avitus Bassianus. Also known as M. Aurelius Antoninus. Emperor of the Roman Empire. Around 220. Young guy. Came to the throne when he was about thirteen or fourteen. Murdered, to the apparent satisfaction of one and all, when he was around seventeen or eighteen. Body thrown into the Tiber."

"Tell me more."

"It's all in Herodian's *History of the Roman Empire*. Read it. I'll just whet your appetite. I won't start with Aeneas and the founding of

Rome, but simply say that Elagabalus' mother was of Phoenician royalty intermarried with Roman royalty. The Phoenician priests worshipped a sun god they called Elagabalus. This word means the Baal of Emesa, their principal city. There was a splendid temple in Emesa to this god. There was no man-made statue of the god's "likeness" in the temple. What it contained was a large, black, conical rock. Reminds one of the Kaaba in Mecca or the Dome of the Rock on the Temple Mount in Jerusalem, doesn't it?

"When Bassianus was about ten or so, he was named priest of the Phoenician sun god and he took the name of the god. Just as today in Europe they take the name of saints. He was a handsome boy and he used to go around in rich, exotic robes. When he performed his ritual duties as priest, he would dance around the altar with flutes and all kinds of instruments playing. Frenzied. Orgiastic.

"Declared emperor – an interesting story, but I'll skip it – he made his way to Rome. He refused Roman garb, but dressed in Eastern style. He painted his eyes and rouged his cheeks. He ordered the Roman priests to sacrifice first to the god Elagabalus and then to the local gods. This caused much grumbling, I daresay. Then spectacles galore were laid on. Sacrifices of hecatombs of animals. He danced around jars of spices and wine intermixed with sacrifical blood. Great theater."

"What else?"

"First he married into high Roman society and nobility and then divorced his wife. Then he slept with a Vestal Virgin. The senate forgave and regularized this. Then he divorced the Vestal and married again into the upper crust of Rome.

"After this fun and games, he decided that he wanted to play marriage broker to the gods and get his sun god married to a goddess."

"What on earth could that have meant?"

"Hard to know what he meant by it, but we know what he did. He brought an old and sacred statue of Pallas Athena and had it placed in his palace. The statue depicted the goddess in full armor. After a while, Elagabalus decided the marriage wasn't 'taking,' that his god wasn't pleased by a goddess who was wearing armor.

"He then sent all the way to Carthage for the image of the goddess Urania (the moon). He told the Carthaginians that he was arranging for a marriage between the sun and the moon. Naturally, when you have a marriage, the bride needs a dowry."

"Naturally."

"So he told the Carthaginians that they should supply a proper dowry for Urania from the treasury of her temple."

"Did they?"

"They did. When the statue and the funds got to Rome, Elagabalus set up the two statues together and had public and private feasts and celebrations laid on in honor of this marriage."

"Neat."

"But if you want to hear more, I'll tell you of a recent marriage of the sun and the moon. It involves me. I was the sun!"

10
Carpenter Switches into Latin

"The Queendom (if such a term is an appropriate description of a matriarchy) of Bulghuristan is not recognized as a separate governmental entity by the nations of the world any more than, say, the State of New Hampshire is so recognized. It sits high in the mountains, minimum elevation about 11,000 feet. Its people have been left alone more or less for centuries – India has hassled them lately – and are largely independent of what goes on at the lower, surrounding elevations. Bulghuri culture was brought to the attention of Western scholars by the discoveries of Aurel Stein. The religion of the Bulghuris is a mixture of Mahayana Buddhism, Zoroastrianism, and Sunni Islam, together with some primitive practices that antedate all of these. The capital is Madoof.

"The population of about five thousand is ruled (I'm not sure in what sense; they keep a lot of things to themselves) by a woman who is known as the Moon of Bulghuristan. Rumors had it that she was well into her fifties and that she had a degree in Greats from Girton College, Cambridge. I found her not unattractive. I was married to her for a week or so. Put the word married in quotes. A symbolic marriage performed under compulsion."

"You committed bigamy, then?"

"No problem by Bulghuri lights. Polygamy and polyandry are rare, but not illegal there."

"What sort of compulsion?"

"The thing was this. A primitive story in Bulghuri history has it that the nation or the tribe was founded by a stranger appearing in the remote Bulghuri valley and taking one of the local maidens to wife. This story was conflated with the even more ancient and widespread myth that the joining of the sun and the moon was the beginning of things. This story was (and still is) reenacted from time to time as part of a state ritual. A Fourth of July celebration, you might say. The Bulghuri queen, who is the moon, is married to a stranger, who is the sun."

"How," I asked Carpenter, "do they determine when this celebration is to be held?"

"It's done astrologically. The details are not given out by the priests and shamans. Seems to occur every 19 years or so. But I doubt if it has anything to do with the Metonic cycle."

"How do they select the stranger who is to play the role of the sun?"

"Again, astrologically. You understand that Bulghuristan being so small and so shut in, each and every stranger is known and is essentially under surveillance. I was asked many, many questions. When I was born. At what hour, etc. I suppose the few other strangers were also questioned."

"Why you, then?"

"Why not me? Haven't you ever been selected for jury duty? At any rate, I was chosen and sequestered in a wing of the royal palace for numerous days during which I was 'purified.' Fumigations, special delicacies – the sign of Leo governs the digestion, you know – chanting, that sort of thing."

"Were you drugged?"

"If so, I wasn't aware of it. I made no objection."

"Did you meet the queen during this period?"

"Indeed I did. She came around and we talked. She seemed hungry for any whiff of the outside world she could get. She asked me whether I played bridge. I said I did. We played bridge often. We were partners, East and West, if you like. The other two players were counsellors of state."

"You're putting me on."

"I am not putting you on."

"Tell me," I said to Carpenter, refusing to challenge him, "about your quote marriage unquote to the Moon of Bulghuristan. Did you 'know her,' as Scripture puts it?"

"Yes, indeed, I knew her very well, and you shall hear about it. Write it up. Publish it if you want. I don't have the time. It's a good story if I say so myself. I myself wouldn't have guessed some of its features.

"The date of the marriage ceremony – it had to occur within one lunation of my arrival in Madoof – was determined astrologically. In order to arrive at a felicitous date, the astrologers and shamans, as I told you, asked me more personal questions than the admitting official of an American hospital.

"When the marriage ceremony itself was over – I'll omit the details of that as there are more interesting things to talk about – the wedding guests remained where they were and a feast was spread. The Moon of Bulghuristan and I were taken to an adjacent room, specially prepared for the occasion; a bridal chamber, let us say. I was also given quite beautiful ritual garments to put on, a shirt and a skirt. I was given to put on a metal chain and plaque on which was engraved a six by six magic square. The square invoked the powers of the sun, so they told me, and it was mine to keep. I'll bring it around some day and show you.

"The room was of impressive size, say about thirty by thirty. It had a low ceiling made even lower by gold and silver silk scarves suspended from it. The scarves bore quotations from the Vedic and Bulghuri texts.

"The floor of the room was well rugged, pillowed, and scarfed, and low taborets were placed here and there. Colored pennants flew along the sides of the room. Along one wall, where an altar was set up, there were various figurines and photographs of local and international notabilities – I recognized a photograph of Mahatma Gandhi and one of Franklin Delano Roosevelt, would you believe. A long row of sweet scented votive candles burned in little glasses. They flickered but slightly and provided the only light. In front of the row of candles, there was another row of glasses each half filled with water. These offerings caught and diffused and refracted the candlelight. In front of this row was a brazier of incense. The aroma was pleasant but slightly cloying.

"Along the two other walls, facing each other, were placed large, carved, wooden see-through screens. The first screen concealed, if that's the right word, three musicians who played on a flute, a sistrum, and a small gong. The second screen concealed two official witnesses, one wearing a yellow hat, designating the motif of asceticism and the second a red hat, designating the tantric tradition."

"You mean you had to perform before witnesses?"

"Don't forget, Phil, that this was a state ritual. This was not a matter of private passions. The Welfare of the Community, and all that, depended on it. The success of the crops, the continuty of the queendom, and much more, I suspect."

"Yes, but I should think that you would have been rather inhibited in the performance of your devoirs."

"You shall hear. You shall hear. Don't anticipate."

"I shall hear?"

"Well, given your sensitivity, I'll relate the raunchy parts 'in the decent obscurity of a learned language,' as Gibbon put it.

"The queen and I were seated on pillows about three feet apart in the center of the room. We were attended by two crones, of high social rank, presumably well experienced in this sort of thing. But how could they be if it occurred once in nineteen years? Anyway, they were older than the queen, who, as I told you was around fifty. One of the attendants took out a set of seven dice and went behind the witness screen. She cast the dice (I couldn't see her do so, but I heard about it later) and the outcome was interpreted as indicating which of the numerous positions of coupling would be the most felicitous on this occasion."

"Which one did you draw?"

"In America it would be called, vulgarly, 'horse and rider.' In Bulghuristan, it's called 'bull and cow.'"

"I assume you speak some Bulghuristanian, but this seems rather specialized. How did they indicate to you that horse and rider was to be the modus operandi?"

"Hanging on the wall was a large colored chart. I'm sure you've seen such charts that depict all the yogic positions? Yes? Well, this was a chart that depicted the canonical modes of copulation, and 'bull and cow' was simply pointed out to us both. The Moon and I nodded in comprehension.

"The attendants then gave us both some kind of sweetmeat to eat. The lute player plucked a bit louder, or so it seemed. The sistrum hissed. The gong sounded, but rarely. The attendant stood the Queen up and removed her skirt. Her headdress, her upper garment and her ritual slippers were left on. A murmur went up from behind the witness screen. Sounds of approval.

"The Queen's substantial mons veneris was depilated after the manner of the high topiary art in the gardens of Versailles. There resulted a crescent which was powdered silver. The Queen, then, was the moon. Indeed she was, and her crescent sparkled in the light of the flickering candles and in the spectra of the water glasses. I was moved by the sight. A nice touch, I thought, very nice, and I wondered whether it was prescribed ritually or was simply the Queen's own contribution to the ceremony."

"Which do you think it was?"

"The latter. A satirical contribution. I found she had a pixie side to her character.

"To go on. The attendants prepared a mound of pillows and spread a white scarf over it. The Queen was placed on the mound belly-bumps, as we kids used to say back in Contoocook when we went coasting in the winter, and her olive orbs took on the abstract geometric quality produced by the sculptors Malliol and Brancusi.

There were further sounds of approval from behind the witness screen.

"I myself reacted to this display in a positive fashion, after the manner of males. My attendant stood me up and removed my skirt. More sounds of approval. Most gratifying to the ego, I must say. A vote of confidence. The prime minister in the British Parliament would have been pleased with less support."

"Did they remove your eyeglasses?"

"No. I wouldn't have allowed that. The visual erotic dimension and all that. Besides, with my nearsightedness, I had to get my priorities straight, so to speak, when it came to the horse and rider.

"I was seated again. Half-masks, silk, were placed over our faces, The Queen's bore the stylized outline of a cow. Mine was that of a bull."

I objected. "I thought you were the sun and the moon."

"So we were, but the basic elements are often transformed and conflated in the way I've described. Animals, minerals, gods, planets. See Sir James Frazer's *Golden Bough*, Volume Four, where he mentions animal masks as part of a solemn rite performed by the kings and queens of Knossos. Knossos was much further west, of course, and much earlier."

"Go on."

"Well, the queen's attendant dipped her hand into a bowl of spiced oil and massaged the queen's orbs with her open palm. The queen responded with a periodic flexing of her gluteal muscles. Her hips fell into copulatory synchronicity. It was paradise to watch and almost beyond bearing.

"At the same time, my attendant massaged my member with a fine aromatic powder. She pronounced a spell over it, making applications (so it was explained to me later) to the planets Jupiter and Venus as governors of the ritual. A fine example of astral magic, if I may venture my opinion. The attendants' chanting continued. My member had been standing aloft these five minutes and now it felt to me as though it might stand erect forever."

"A disabling condition, I should think. I mean in the long run. What happened then?"

"I was urged to my knees by the queen's attendant; all the while my own attendant was powdering and massaging my member. Then the queen's attendant. . . ."

Here, Carpenter continued his narrative in Latin. Due to my inability to handle this language properly, a number of sentences will be omitted here.

"How could you hold out?"

"Magic. That's what it was. Absolute magic. The spells, the fragrances – aromatherapy no doubt is what they would call it today – the music. With the Bulghuris, the erotic element goes beyond Western love and sentiment. Erotics are part of social and agricultural policy as well as a part of religious tradition. Erotics are far too important a thing to be left to the random processes of Cupid's arrows or to be allowed to degenerate to the meaningless concatenated conjunctions now seen in our part of the world."

"What happened next?"

"When the attendant, feeling my member, judged that it had been primed sufficiently, she slipped on it a little golden ring, embossed with a sol motif and the Arabic word *dhahab* (gold), the ring attached to a bit of an open woven socklet – one size fits all. Clever, no? Then, fully and truly, I was the sun. The Sun was ready to approach the Moon.

"My attendant gave me a slight push forward and I entered the Moon, à la horse and rider. I was King Krishna entering the Moon and, as it says in the text, about to supply life juice to all the vegetables.

"The Queen, no virgin she, did her part, amply, nobly, artfully, generously, but in silence; and I was kept so stiffened by the surrounding aura of magic that I rode her down. Yes, I rode her down. The minutes wore on. The attendants who now waited behind the screen with the witnesses, the musicians behind their screen, all murmured.

"Finally, my Queen, my Moon, my royal bridge partner who had previously maintained silence, now called out in the perfect accents of Cambridge University, 'Let's get on with it, for heaven's sake. Shall we?'

"When I heard her silence broken, it so affected me that I. . . ."

Here, again, Carpenter made a smooth transition to Latin. Several sentences are omitted.

"I fell back exhausted. After a decent interval, the attendants came out from behind the screen. They picked up the white scarf on which the Sun and the Moon had played out the ancient drama and rubbed a kind of rouge into it as symbolic evidence that the Moon was a virgin whose virginity recurred perpetually. They carried the scarf over to the witnesses. The witnesses examined the scarf, approved what they saw, and went into the adjacent banqueting hall and displayed the scarf to the assembled feasting wedding guests. A shout arose. Gongs sounded. Shortly thereafter, I could hear fireworks being shot off outside.

"Shams – the Sun (me) and Qamar – the moon (the queen) were led back to the banqueting hall, and fed morsels and tid-bits by their two attendants. An additional three hours passed of banqueting, music, and ritual dances.

"But the affair as a whole was not quite over. The next day, a male infant was brought forth from the bed of a newly delivered peasant woman. The infant was laid on the queen's dry breast so that she might give it symbolic suck. In ten days or so (during which time I was still incommunicado and played bridge), the infant was circumcised and named Carpenter Iskander Bulghuri-Ran, and declared to be of the queen's descent. He would be raised in the Royal Palace. The real parents were given a generous payment and the rights of perpetual dual parenthood. I had known about the ceremonial marriage of the sun and moon, but the pseudo-childbirth was news to me."

Carpenter paused in his narration.

"I don't believe you. You've been reading Rider Haggard. All this happened? You swear it? You're hoaxing me. This is the twentieth century!"

"Just as I described it. I will swear it on any book you like. The *Bible*. The *Koran*. On Hermes Trismegistus. Euclid. The *Meditations* of Marcus Aurelius. The *Statutes of the Commonwealth of Massachusetts*. You name it."

"Hmmm. And where does mathematics come into this?"

"It's a fine example of applied mathematics. You fellows tend to think that applied mathematics must be physics, economics, business, technology. Statistics. Computers. War. But mathematics can and has been applied to all aspects of life and in different ways. When the Bulghuri astrologers determined a felicitous day from the sun and moon to join on earth, what was that if not applied mathematics? When they cast dice to determine an appropriate copulative position, that was applied mathematics. When they hung a magic square around my neck, one that represented the sun and added up to my zodiacal sign, that was applied mathematics.

"Truth or falsity as we conceive of it in the West was irrelevant. It wasn't the issue. What was important was the expression of the unity of the whole as seen against the apparent chaos of the universe. The organic and inorganic worlds, the stellar worlds were seen as united. And this is the hope even in today's standard,

Western science, a good deal of which will surely be laughed at five hundred years down the turnpike."

"Do you mind if I tell your story, making it anonymous of course, to a couple of ethno-mathematicians I know? They believe in ethno-education. I'd like their reaction to what you've told me."

"Be my guest. Publish it, as I've suggested. Despite all the relativism that's around today, I doubt if what you write will get reprinted in elementary textbooks."

"What happened to the child?"

"I don't really know. I expect he was trained for a high administrative post in the palace."

"Did you get the manuscript you were looking for?"

"No. But I got a story, didn't I?"

Several weeks later, I received through the university mail a little package from Carpenter containing a silver chain and medallion. On the medallion was engraved this arrangement of numbers:

Dhahab

11	63	5	67	69	1
13	21	53	55	15	59
37	27	31	29	45	47
35	39	43	41	33	25
49	57	19	17	51	23
71	9	65	7	3	61

A short note from Carpenter provided an "explanation": "The Arabic word on the top means gold (the sun). The numbers are in 15th century arabic numerals and they are the progression of odd numbers from 1 to 71. Each row, column and major diagonal adds up to 216. The number 216 is the numerical value of 'Lion' (Leo). There are 14 such sums, and 14 is the numerical value of gold = lion = sun. The numerical values of 'lion,' etc., relate to the spelling in Hebrew, which had a certain primal force in ancient alchemy."

11
A Lead Develops

I have taken a very long time indeed to get to the matter of the ascription of Napoleon's Theorem. Brevity is rarely a virtue in storytelling. Time is not of the essence. But now, at last, I'm getting close.

I was having lunch with Carpenter one spring day. He'd asked me a simple question, whether it was possible to derive the infinite series for the sine of an angle without the use of calculus. His question had something to do with his own researches into the history of ancient mathematics from India. I answered him in the affirmative and he was quite pleased with what he heard.

"In return, may I now bother you with a question, Alex?"

"'Ask what you choose, for you have come to men who know everything." Apollonius of Tyana, Book III."

"Everything?"

"Well, everything before 500 AD, let us say to be modest. After that, knowledge spotty. Very. Vast deserts of ignorance. And moderately vast indifference. The sweetness of ancient thought binds one, does it not?"

"But mightn't I hit an oasis of knowledge?"

"It's not impossible."

"Then, my question is, who discovered Napoleon's Theorem?"

"What on earth is Napoleon's Theorem?" Carpenter asked me.

I explained it to him on the back of a napkin.

"Napoleon, as in Napoleon Bonaparte?"

"The same." Then I went on to explain what I knew of the matter, telling him the part about Napoleon that is contained in the first chapter of this book.

"Bonaparte is contemporary history to me," Carpenter opined, using the elevated tone that professors sometimes use when lecturing. "I have little use for the contemporary. I've practically no responsibility for it, unless, somehow, with your recent theories of time, you can arrange for the present and the future to influence the past. Why do you care to know?"

"Frivolous curiosity, really. But honestly aroused. Since I was a kid. I've worked on the theorem recently, and when I came to write up my work, I wanted to give fairly extensive references. I looked into it a bit and came up against a stone wall of silence."

"I see. I take it you've discarded the obvious answer?"

"Which is?"

"That Napoleon's Theorem was discovered by Napoleon."

"It's a strong possibility but we have nothing concrete to back it up."

"What reasons do you have for doubting the ascription?" Carpenter then asked me.

"It's an unlikely solution. Most of Newton's theorems were not discovered by Newton. Same for Gauss. The origins of the famous theorem of Pythagoras, so you historical guys have pointed out, are lost in the sands of second millennium Egypt, if not in the ancient orient.

"Why Napoleon should have thought up Napoleon's Theorem beats me. Did Napoleon create the pastries that bear his name? Did Napoleon press grapes for Napoleon Brandy? Did he sauté the chicken for Chicken Marengo? Furthermore, such a simple and obvious solution to the problem would be discouraging. An anticlimax."

"Very true, Phil. Such simplicity would be very naughty. Perverse. It's quite easy to arrive at the platonic concept of Chicken Marengo without the necessity of vast armies having fought the

Battle of Marengo. Tolstoy even suggested that the Napoleonic Age would have existed without Napoleon."

"Precisely."

"But let's separate two problems here. The first problem is, who originally discovered or publicized the theorem? This problem is hard; the answer may never be known. The second problem is, how did the theorem, now known by the name of Napoleon, acquire that name? That is somewhat easier."

"I should think so."

We ate on for a bit in silence. Then Carpenter said to me, very much as Holmes to Watson, "The problem intrigues. Yes, it intrigues. Not exactly my dish of tea. But it has features of interest and a certain charm. I'll take on the inquiry. A dip in the cold waters of the wrong (for me) century may have astringent virtues."

"Splendid. You understand, of course, that the answer makes not the slightest difference to my mathematical work?"

"I understand perfectly. A mere grace note to a footnote? Ars gratia artis, that sort of thing? No apologies required. The intellect must have its playful moments. In that way its strength is renewed."

Several weeks passed before Carpenter and I had lunch again. I had found by experience that there was little point in nudging him for information; if he had any for me, it would come out naturally in the flow of conversation. And it did.

"I don't suppose that you've heard of the *Toparcha Gothicus*, have you?"

"You suppose correctly. Tell me about it."

"Medieval Ukranian history. And I don't suppose you've ever heard of Karl Benedikt Hase, have you? "

"Your supposition is right on target. Tell me."

"Great scholar. Great classicist. Great ladies' man. Also a forger. He forged several fragments of the *Toparcha Gothicus*. At least

Sevčenko thinks so."

"Who's Sevčenko?"

"At Harvard. Department of Ukranian Studies."

"Why do you bring this up?"

"Well, you asked me about Napoleon's Theorem a while back. I have a lead I think you might follow up on your own. Go talk to Sevčenko perhaps."

"What's the connection to Napoleon?"

"Hase, I think, had an affair with Hortense, Napoleon's sister-in-law."

"So?"

"More to the point, Hase also, for a while, tutored Hortense's two young sons. History, classics, mathematics."

"I still don't see the connection."

"Think about it a bit. Read Sevčenko's article on Hase. Hortense's two sons were called Napoleon-Louis and Louis-Napoleon."

12
Napoleon's Circle

In order to explain the relevance of Karl Benedikt Hase to the problem I had posed to myself, I should really begin by painting a miniature picture of Paris at the time of Le Grand Empire.

On the evening of February 11, 1812, at a costume ball in the Tuilleries, a woman of twenty-eight, her face masked and her lovely figure draped magnificently in silver cloth, made a grand entrance. She represented the Peruvian High Priestess of the Sun (the allegorical interpretation of which need not concern us), and she was accompanied by a retinue of young women and men clad similarly, though somewhat less extravagantly. The group executed a carefully choreographed and rehearsed ballet-masque.

Later in the evening, the young woman was approached by a short man wearing a domino.

"Madame," he said, "you dazzle my eyes."

"Sir," she replied, "I could be a prize, covered as I am with diamonds."

"But the really priceless diamond is the one hidden by your costume."

The Priestess of the Sun was Hortense de Beauharnais Bonaparte, lately Queen of Holland, and simultaneously the Emperor Napoleon's step-daughter and his sister-in-law. The domino was the Emperor himself. The ball occurred at the height of Le Grand Empire. How cloying this conversation, recorded in Hortense's autobiography, seems to our present unromantic sensibilities!

The rise in a few short years of Napoleon Bonaparte from the son of an insignificant Corsican squire to Emperor of France and master of a good fraction of Europe, though an absolutely incredible story, is a fairly well known one. What is equally incredible and somewhat less well known is that Napoleon was one of eight children, five boys and three girls, and that as he rose, he carried all his brothers and sisters with him upwards. In one of the most brazen instances of nepotism known to history, he managed to insert them all into the high aristocratic and regal places of Europe.

The Napoleon story continues to haunt the French imagination, if not the imagination of the entire world. Thousands of books have been written about Napoleon. As this story is central to the solution of what I came to call the Napoleon Enigma, some of it must be recalled here.

To place the action properly, we need to make an inventory of the children of Maria-Letizia and Carlo Bonaparte, Napoleon's mother and father. In order of arrival they were: Joseph (Giuseppe), Napoleon, Lucien (Luciano), Elisa (Maria-Anna), Louis (Luigi), Caroline (Maria Annunziata), Pauline (Maria-Paola), and finally, Jérôme (Girolamo).

The Napoleon in this list, of course, is Napoleon I, Emperor of France. This obvious fact is mentioned because, without further modification, the name Napoleon can be, as we shall see, rather ambiguous. There are "Napoleon this-es and "Napoleon" thats. The nomenclature is confusing and cries out for color-coding at the very least.

Joseph was King of Spain. Lucien was Prince of Canino. Elisa was the Grand Duchess of Tuscany. Jérôme was King of Westphalia. Caroline was married to Joachim Murat and became Queen of Naples. Pauline was Duchess of Guastalla and married Camillo, Prince Borghese. Finally, Louis was placed on the throne of Holland in 1806. His reign was brief: he abdicated in 1810.

This massive invasion of the aristocracy by the members of a single middle-class family spelled the beginning of the end of the kings and queens of Europe functioning in the role that seemed long established and sanctioned by God. If, in retrospect, the invasion now seems incredible, it was due less to the hypnotic individual genius of Napoleon than to the fact that the aristocracy had outlived its historic function and was about to crack open. In fact, the French Revolution of 1789 had sliced it open. And, irony of ironies, the aristocracy was, under Napoleon, about to be restored by a genius who, as was once said of Oscar Wilde a century later, was *bourgeois malgré lui*.

We need not follow the marriages of these eight brothers and sisters in all their complexities, but several wives must be identified carefully. The Emperor Napoleon's first wife was Josephine Beauharnais. Napoleon was, in fact, Josephine's second husband, her first being Alexandre Vicomte de Beauharnais, by whom she had two children: Eugène and Hortense de Beauharnais. Josephine fell widow to the guillotine.

Hortense, who became Napoleon's step-daughter upon his marriage to Josephine, herself married Napoleon's brother Louis, and, in so doing, became Napoleon's sister-in-law as well. This marriage was arranged according to the laws of "palace biology." At the time, Napoleon had no male descendants, and Josephine pressured one and all into keeping as much control within the family as possible. Some people married money, some married genealogy; ideally, one married both.

Louis Bonaparte and Hortense had three children, acknowledged publicly as such, but the legitimacy of several of them was considered moot by the public and by Louis himself. In order of appearance, their children were Napoleon Charles, Napoleon Louis, and Louis Napoleon. Does not the head whirl with the permutations of these few names? Napoleon Charles, whom the Emperor at one time proposed adopting as his own son and successor, died as a young boy. Louis Napoleon, the youngest, grew up to be Emperor Napoleon III of the Second Empire and the husband of Empress Eugénie. We shall focus on the middle son, Napoleon Louis.

It was clear that the Emperor Napoleon loved Hortense greatly. There were rumors, politically inspired for the most part, that Hortense's first son, Napoleon-Charles, was the Emperor's child.

In 1806 the Louis Bonapartes, the newly designated King and Queen of Holland, moved into Amsterdam, at that time the capital of Holland, with a retinue of ten waiting ladies, two equeries, three priests, two physicians, and a librarian.

Husband Louis was the devout one of the family, and was

increasingly so as he grew older and as his personal troubles multiplied. Hortense, on the contrary, spent a good deal of time with books, letters, intellectuals, free thinkers, and anti-clericals. She painted, she wrote songs. Later on in life she wrote a three-volume set of memoirs. She must have found a librarian a congenial and important addition to her household.

The relationship between Louis Bonaparte and his wife Hortense de Beauharnais was a failure from the start. The gossip was that while Louis was with the army in Egypt, he had picked up a disability from a fille-de-joie and, improperly cured, this had led to various complications that crippled him increasingly. (Louis' brother, the Emperor, called him a paralytic.)

Faced with a wife who was beautiful, spirited, clever, and above all, ambitious, Louis became paranoid. He used to take a candle and look under the bed for Hortense's real or imaginary lovers. It was almost a certainty, given his paranoia and his frequent absences seeking health at the spas of Europe, that life with Louis would have driven Hortense into more cheerful arms. One set of arms belonged to Charles de Flahaut. She was infatuated with him. In 1811, four months before the ball, she had an illegitimate son by de Flahaut, whom she kept unpublicized for many years.

Louis saw that Holland's commercial life was inextricably bound up with that of England. But England was Napoleon's enemy. As its king, Louis wanted Holland to prosper. He did nothing to make life hard for the English. Infuriated, Napoleon took over. Louis' role collapsed, his relations with his brother Napoleon deteriorated, and he abdicated in 1810. After this date, he and Hortense essentially lived apart. For a while, Hortense and her two sons were in Paris. Louis was here, he was there. It hardly mattered.

In the meantime, the boys were growing.

13
Charles-Benoit Hase and the Fickle Moon

When Napoleon-Louis was about seven years of age, his uncle, the Emperor, decided that the time had come to get a good tutor for the boys. The best in the land, of course, and Napoleon, who had drawn about him the most brilliant intellectuals and scientists and artists in France, had access to what was best.

As a consequence of the Emperor's concern for his nephews, in September 1812, a week before Napoleon's army knocked at the gates of Moscow, a certain Charles-Benoit Hase, perhaps the leading classicist of his day, presented himself at the door of Queen Hortense and her two boys (after Louis' abdication Hortense was often called Queen as an affectionate honor). Hase was to be schoolmaster, particularly for the oldest, Napoleon Louis. To arrive at a proper idea of what this appointment amounted to, we need a parallel: it would be as though Queen Elizabeth II had engaged Albert Einstein to teach young Prince Charles his multiplication tables.

Charles-Benoit Hase, né Karl Benedikt Hase (1780–1864), was born a German but lived most of his life in Paris. Hase was a very famous scholar of Classical Greek and Byzantine literature. He was professor at the École Polytechnique and Conservateur des Manuscrits at the Bibliothèque Nationale. He put out an edition of the *Historia* of Leo Diaconus. He did a number of magnificent textual restorations. One manuscript, that of Johannes Lydus, had been hidden for decades in a wine barrel in a monastery, and its recovery and restoration could be worked into a romance worthy of Sir Walter Scott or Umberto Eco. He wrote intelligently on Byzantine astrolabes, so he must have known a bit of mathematics. This was all part of his career prior to that of Royal Tutor.

Hase taught the children of Hortense from about 1812 through 1815. (Le Grand Empire was collapsing, but life goes on. How many children in Leningrad took music and ballet lessons while the city was under seige? You'd be surprised.)

All this information can be found in your encyclopedia, if your encyclopedia is sufficiently large and sufficiently old. What you will not find are the following facts which lift Hase out of the dry-as-dust category.

One: Monsieur Hase was a man with an enormous appetite for the amatory arts and pastimes.

Two: He had an affair with Queen Hortense.

Three: Monsieur Hase left a very blunt and scandalous secret diary, written in a kind of private Greek language, in which these things are implied. Hase's secret diary has been lost, but some of the less scandalous parts of it were copied out and are available.

Four: Monsieur Hase was a forger.

I turn to Fact Four. Hase was not a counterfeiter of money or a forger of signatures on cheques. He was a forger within his scholarly profession. At least modern scholarly opinion believes he was.

In 1819, in an annotated edition of the *History* of Leo Diaconus, Hase inserted three Greek fragments, previously unpublished, which bear upon the history of the Crimea in the year 989. These fragments of history were so skillfully and cleverly composed that their authenticity was unquestioned for fifty years; even now, the case against Hase has not been secured at the 100% level of certainty.

A Gilbert and Sullivan buff might interpolate here: it would seem that Hase provided sufficient corroborative detail to provide artistic verisimilitude.

What was the moral climate of the day? Money. Power. Glory. Amorous adventures. The idea of "forsaking all others till death do us part" stressed in the English *Book of Common Prayer* was not an ideal when one crossed over to Calais. The marriage bond was not considered operative in a proprietary sense.

If the world at the seats of power was morally flexible, the world at the seats of scholarship was only slightly less so. The Napoleonic armies plundered the libraries and museums of Europe and brought much material to Paris. Scholars often treated library material as though they personally owned it. The younger Champollion of the Rosetta Stone connection, for example, sold parchments and papyri belonging to the Bibliothèque Nationale. In a brisk market, forgeries of art and ancient documents proliferated.

It is not relevant to the present document to speculate on why Hase, a man with a record of brilliant accomplishments, should have found it necessary to indulge in forgery. Of course it does indicate a person who is enlivened by practical-joke-making. It is relevant to take up the available portions of his diary, in particular the pages which include a tiny scribbled diagram composed of four triangles, and to reconstruct a scene.

The date: July 29, 1813. The place: Hortense's residence in Paris, children's wing. Her husband, Louis Bonaparte, is living quietly abroad, probably in Graz.

"And what did you teach my little Prince today, Herr Hase?"

"Monsieur Hase, if your Gracious Majesty will allow it. Among the French, I intend to be a Frenchman."

"You are very right to want to do so. To be French is to be a Citizen of the Universe."

"Thank you, Madame. I taught your Prince history, Madame. Thucydides. It went well. We have nearly completed that author."

"I am glad. You know, our Emperor says that history is the one true philosophy."

"And so it is, Madame."

"What portion of Thucydides did you teach?"

"We read the disastrous Siege of Syracuse by the Athenians. The blundering, dilatory strategy of Nicias, the leader of the Athenian fleet."

"Oh, Hase, I suppose we must learn to live with our disasters. Our Emperor lives with his and this teaches us fortitude. In what year was this disaster?"

"Indeed we must, Madame. It came about in the year 413. *Avant J.-C., naturellement.*"

"And what moral did you derive for my son in this chapter of history?"

"*Il faut battre le fer pendant qu'il est chaude.*"

"And yourself, Monsieur, what moral for yourself? Surely a teacher must grow even as he teaches."

"Even so, Madame. For myself, I have learned that the August Moon is fickle."

"The Moon? How do you know this, Monsieur le Professeur?"

"Because Nicias, the Athenian, was misled by the moon. In August of the year I mentioned, there was an eclipse of the moon, quite visible in Syracuse. And his augers and soothsayers said to him, "Delay, O Nicias." And 'thrice nine days' did Nicias tarry. It led him to defeat."

"And how does this strange story apply to you?"

"Oh, Madame, you have known my heart for these many months. And while our Emperor is the sun, I know that you, Madame, are the silver-gowned moon."

"Ah, Monsieur, the cruel world has cast shadows on this moon's silver surface. Do not rush my wounded heart with your impetuous desires. Tell me more about my little boy."

"Your Prince, Madame, has lately discovered a wonderful aspect of geometrical nature which he revealed to me. It has not been known before, and to think: only nine years of age. I have assured your Prince that his discovery would be called 'Napoleon's Theorem' for all time. He is a most excellent student."

"And you, Monsieur Hase, a most wonderful Master. *A demain*, then?"

"Indeed, Madame, *demain*."

III

The Man Who Began His Lectures with "Namely"

L'amour s'en va
L'amour s'en va
Comme cette eau courante
Comme l'Esperance est violente

— G. Apollinaire
Le Pont Mirabeau

1
Variations on the Pathetic Fallacy

In 1936 I fell in love with Elisabeth Bergner. At that time I was a schoolboy of thirteen marching off each morning with Latin, French, and geometry books in my briefcase. Elisabeth Bergner was thirty-six. She was then at the height of her career as an actress. The difference of twenty-three years was an irrelevance. I fell in love with her much as I had fallen in love two years earlier with Mozart's G-Minor Symphony. Both the symphony and the actress lay at the narrow edge between the animate and the abstract worlds.

I remember going to see her in *Escape Me Never*. I can remember which movie house. I remember thinking that the inversion of "Never" and "Escape" from the usual order was very sophisticated, and I attributed this to her. I can see her smallish figure, her page-boy haircut, her puckish face and sultry eyes – a strange mixture, when you come right down to it. I remember very little about the movie. I don't know what the plot was. Most of it probably went straight over my head at the time. In the intervening years I have never seen it again.

As a result of this movie, I fell in love, as I have said. I followed Bergner's career in the papers and magazines. I knew she had played in Eugene O'Neill's *Strange Interlude*, another one of those incomprehensible grown-up things. I knew that she would be playing in *The Tempest*. I did not see her in it. Nor did I see the two movies she made somewhat later. Yet my love was steady.

I was not a member of her fan club, if ever she had one; I doubt it, for she was in the limelight for only a few years. I did not spend hours at her stage door waiting for a glimpse, or an autograph, or a smile, or a button ripped brutally from her sleeve. I did not pin up her pictures on my bedroom wall. Pale behavior, you may think, for an ardent youth. Of what then did this love consist? Fundamentally, I suppose, it was self-love.

Elisabeth Bergner

I loved her because I fancied she loved me. She knew me, she knew who I was, she knew where I lived. I loved her because I fancied she loved what I loved. I loved the G-Minor Symphony, she loved the G-Minor Symphony. I loved the mountains, she loved the mountains. I loved mathematics, Elisabeth Bergner obviously loved mathematics. My fate was her fate. I had projected myself onto her and she reflected back, like the moon, or lately, like the signs at night on the superhighway.

There is a figure of speech known as the pathetic fallacy. This is where human feelings are ascribed to inanimate nature; for example, "the raging sea," "the devouring flame." The sea, being inanimate, cannot really rage. But writers, perceiving its wildness and dangers, set up a parallel to human behavior. In the same way, I had promulgated a kind of pathetic fallacy.

Elisabeth Bergner loves me. How can this be? Insofar as she is part of the inanimate world of symbols, she can neither know me nor love me. Since Elisabeth Bergner loves me, I love her. How can this be? How can I love an abstraction? If she were suddenly to materialize I might find that the real person was stupid, jealous, or stingy. She, for her part, would take one look and see that I was merely a boy of thirteen.

Shortly thereafter, Bergner disappeared from the limelight. I heard she settled in London. My infatuation with her lay dormant for years.

2
Lindner

Forty years later I wrote a piece that echoed some of these feelings. Here it is.

★ ★ ★

In 1950, I earned my degree and was working with one of my professors as a post-doctoral fellow. Call him Lindner. Vassily Lindner. At that time Lindner was fifty-five. He had an international reputation in science. He was brilliant but eccentric. He was a refugee from Poland; the war years had been ghastly. He had never married.

It was part of the arrangement that I work an hour or an hour and a half a day with him. Now this was the manner of our working. During the week we worked at the office. On weekends we worked in his flat. We would sit down together at a desk, and Lindner would explain a piece of theory he was developing.

"Do you understand? Do you like? Is clear? Shall I say again? You get point?"

He would then write down a few more lines and a similar recital would occur.

"You see the difficulty? Is not clever? This is correct, no? We check other book. Look at so-and-so's paper on topic. Shall I present to you again?"

After ten minutes Lindner would get up and fix himself a cup of tea.

"You want tea? You want Coke?"

After twenty minutes, Lindner would call up Washington, "Hallo, Dr. Smith. Lindner speaking. You know this my paper on subject. . . ."

After thirty minutes of mathematics, Lindner would call up a Polish stockbroker he knew in New York and for ten solid minutes they would buy and sell shares in Polish. Then back to me.

"You check equation? Is correct? You can generalize? Maybe we set up a big computation? Is fewer hypotheses?"

Then, out to the hall. Back. Then to the men's room. Back to me. Up to the library to check a fact. Back to the telephone. Back to me.

"Draw figure. Is always useful."

To the newspaper to check the movies. Back to me. Call up the secretary who was sick with a cold.

He might call me up at home at 11:30 PM.

"Hallo Feeooo? [his way of pronouncing "Phil" – the soft Polish L, I always thought]. You remember formula? Shall I say over phone? Do I wake you up? Is all right to speak now?"

On Sunday mornings we often worked at Lindner's place. He had a cold water flat in a seamy part of town. In the winter, he would turn on the jets of his two-burner stove and we would work in the kitchen. He was earning plenty of money at this time, but the experiences of the past were not easily shaken off.

I was never quite sure precisely what my function was. Ostensibly, I was equal parts scientific secretary, confidant, checker, computer, assistant theorizer, and leg man. I was never quite sure why he needed me or what I contributed to his work. As we sat at his desk or at his kitchen table, my mind wandered frequently. As he rambled on, I found myself doing my own work. I developed my own theories. I found that my intuitions were different than his, and so were my aesthetic values. He liked me and I him. Even as I was screaming and yelling all the while, I was learning how to do research. I stuck it out for two years, but it finally drove me up the wall.

Halfway along the second year, Lindner told me that he was thinking seriously of getting married. "What do you think? Is not good idea? You will like."

The whole thing sounded absurd to me. By that time I was already married, and I knew that this man would drive any woman crazy in five minutes. Of course I didn't let him know what I thought. I played the judicious, conservative parent and pompously suggested, as Polonius might have, that I should like to meet his intended. He said, "Yes of course. She comes next weekend. You will see. I think is good thing."

He had been introduced to Margarete by a third party who was interested in promoting the match. She was a recent widow, had no children and she was somewhat younger than Lindner. She came originally from Vienna, and her war-years wanderings were not unlike his. She was working in a hat shop in New York. They had been together on three or four occasions in New York, and now she was coming to his place to look him over "in the field," as it were.

On that cold Sunday morning in December I rang Lindner's doorbell with some hesitation. He came to the door, with a wide smile. "Ah, Feeooo, I am so happy to see you. Margarete is here. She looks to see you. You will like. I know. Come in. She is in kitchen."

We walked through the cold front hall and cold front room into the steamy kitchen. Margarete was sitting on a chair looking at the burning gas jets and smoking a cigarette. In that moment I saw a page-boy haircut and I saw eyes and mouth that reminded me of Elisabeth Bergner. I was embarrassed as I stepped forward. Margarete jumped up and threw her arms around me and kissed me.

"I have heard all about you. So. Let me look at you. You are one of Vassily's scientific children, isn't it? [There was another post-doctoral, Milton Armour, who worked with Lindner in the same way that I did.] Well, you poor boy. I hope you don't let Vassily take advantage of you. Vassily, why do you drag him out into the cold on Sunday. Couldn't it wait till tomorrow?"

To my American ears she spoke just like Elisabeth Bergner. I could see that Lindner was very happy. We talked for a short while, and then Lindner said: "O.K., Margarete. Now you two have met. Now we go to the front room for a short while and work."

He pulled me into the front room, and we worked for an hour in the cold (I remember keeping my heavy coat on) while Margarete stayed in the kitchen and read the Sunday paper by the gas jets.

When we were through, I went to say goodbye to Margarete. She came to the front door with me. Lindner went back to the kitchen to fuss with a cup of tea or something.

"Well," she asked me bluntly, "do I have your approval?" I hesitated to answer her question.

"You are beautiful," I said. "You remind me of Elisabeth Bergner." I didn't anticipate – I could not have anticipated her response. She cried.

When she had pulled herself together and dried her eyes she said, "You are mocking me."

"No. It's true."

I walked down the steps feeling like a clod. They were married the following week. It worked. Twenty-five years later, I dedicated a book to them both.

$\star \quad \star \quad \star$

In writing these recollections I recalled a marvelous portrait of Elisabeth Bergner taken in 1935 by Edward Steichen. It is the full profile of a uniquely beautiful woman. The photographer set strong lights behind the figure to give a silhouette effect. Her hair was cut short.

Her eyebrows were pencilled. She had long lashes and heavy lids; her nose was slightly retroussé. Her lips were half open as though the camera shutter had caught a gasp. She wore sweater and slacks. Her knees were up and her hands clasped her ankles. Her nervous vitality was restrained momentarily.

At the same time, my mind performed an act of incarnation that made possible a leap from symbol to flesh. The real Elisabeth Bergner, if alive, was now seventy-five. I was fifty-two. Steichen's picture was now the melancholy reminder of what was and no longer is.

I found her name in a book on the European film industry. Here is what it said: "Liesel Bergner, driven out of Germany at the time of Hitler together with many fine performers. . . ." The flame devours. Note: Liesel, not Elisabeth. The nickname cuts into me. "Liesel" brings to my mind her father and her mother; it suggests a small child marching off to school with a lunch box.

What was her real history? Did she have a family? Did she go to work for a theatrical agent in London? What made her happy? Had she done what she wanted to do? What did she think about when she was sixty? I don't know. My affair was private, abstract. Nor does it matter. What matters is that she was a mirror.

The sea rages, and therefore God exists. Even in Vienna.

3
Bergman at Brown

Those of my readers who are "in the know" will recognize the equations Vassily Lindner = Stefan Bergman and Margarete Lindner = Edie (Adele) Bergman. Of course, Elisabeth Bergner =

Elisabeth Bergner, the famous actress. The close resemblance of the two surnames is purely accidental.

I am not sure just what got into me when I wrote the Lindner story other than a warm feeling for both Stefan and Edie. At the time, I showed it to several of Bergman's Ph.D. students, who enjoyed it and urged me to publish it.

A few years after Stefan's death, I got up my courage and sent it, somewhat timorously, to Edie. She wrote me back almost immediately that she liked my story, and she added the following bit of personal history which I had not known, and which, in view of what I had written, I found quite remarkable.

In the early twenties, Edie, who was also in her twenties, was in Vienna and she was a bit stage struck. She wanted to be an actress. At that time, there was a quite famous school in Vienna for acting, painting, etc., whose name I have forgotten. One of the teachers of acting in that school was the very young Elisabeth Bergner. Edie enrolled, and had Elisabeth Bergner as one of her teachers. "So you see," she wrote to me, "your perceptions were accurate, I have probably been imitating Bergner ever since. And Bergner was typically Viennese."

I asked Edie what Bergner was like as a teacher. She replied that Bergner was an absolute tyrant. "You must do it this way. I will show you. Don't do it that stupid way. Etc."

Edie shared another memory. In 1922, or thereabouts, a young man who had some drawing ability applied to the graphics department of her school. He was turned down. His name, she said, was Adolf Hitler. "If he had been accepted," she wrote me, "how my own history and the history of the world would have been changed."

It is sad but true that in the past century, war has been a tremendous spur to science and technology. In the past century only? It goes way way back. Didn't Archimedes, the most famous scientist of his day, invent war machines to stay the Roman Legions in their siege of Syracuse (214 BC)? A thousand years prior, didn't the Israelites regret that they didn't have iron weapons, whose technology their enemies the Philistines kept secret? In the late Renaissance, didn't Tartaglia, a famous Italian mathematician, write a book on ballistics, hardly ever mentioned in histories of mathematics, that contained a cautionary warning to the reader?

By the time of World War II, the technologies of radar, sonar, ballistics, bomb-sights, anti-aircraft defense, aeronautics, hydrodynamics, atomic energy, cryptography, and operations research, all important in war making, and all involving mathematics at the deepest levels, were in full development. Government laboratories were expanded greatly. Industries turned their production to the "war effort." And the universities did basic research, production research, and trained up a generation of skilled technologists and theoreticians.

Bergman came from Czestochawa, Poland (then part of Russia), a city about 125 miles southwest of Warsaw. It is the city of the famous Jasna Gora Madonna (the Shrine of the Black Virgin) where he was born in 1895. His father had been a banker and was fairly well-to-do. In 1913 Bergman entered the School of Engineering in Breslau and switched in 1915 to the School of Engineering in Vienna.

Bergman obtained his Ph.D. degree in 1922 at the University of Berlin under the direction of Richard von Mises. I have no idea where he was or how he got through the years 1922 to 1930. From 1930 to 34 he was a *Privatdocent* in Berlin. From 1934 to 1937 he was in Tomsk in Siberia, where he was a professor in the university. From 1937 to 1939 he was in Paris.

The German army entered Czestochawa on September 3, 1939,

MATHEMATICAL ENCOUNTERS OF THE SECOND KIND

and he lost two sisters to the subsequent Holocaust.

Bergman came to the United States in 1939. He was at MIT from 1939 to 1940. It was my freshman year at Harvard. During our first week the poet Archibald MacLeish told my freshman class "The lights are going out all over the world." We sat on the floor in the Freshman Union and shuddered. We had no idea when or if they would go on again.

Bergman lived on a series of short-term appointments. He was at Yeshiva University 1940–41, at Brown University in Providence 1941–45, at Harvard from 1945–1951, at MIT 1951–52. All of these appointments were on "soft money," that is, year-to-year government research contracts. Beginning in the mid-thirties, the country was filling up with refugees from Hitler's Europe; writers, artists, musicians, doctors, lawyers, and scientists came across the ocean. The economic depression was hardly over. Jobs were scarce. Men who had been professors in prestigious European universities took jobs teaching high school. Bergman was lucky with his appointments.

From the summer of 1941 through the academic year 1945–46, Brown University had a Program of Advanced Instruction and Research in Mechanics organized by Dean R.G.D. Richardson. This program was the forerunner of the Division of Applied Mathematics at Brown, established in 1946. The lecturers included Stefan Bergman, Leon Brillouin, Willi Feller, Hilda Geiringer, Withold Hurewicz, Richard von Mises, Otto Neugebauer, F.D. Murnaghan, Hillel Poritzky, William Prager, Hans Reissner, Sergei A. Schelkunoff, I.S. Sokolnikoff, and J.D. Tamarkin. The program was supported by the Rockefeller Foundation. The faculty consisted largely of refugees. It was one of the most brilliant groups of mathematicians ever assembled.

How did this training at Brown look to a student in the summer of 1942? I can't say. I wasn't there, but I can call on the words of

Professor Clifford Truesdell, now emeritus from Johns Hopkins, who was one of the 110 students and 45 postdoctoral fellows. In a letter to his grandmother Truesdell wrote a series of hypercritical sketches of the faculty. (All students are hypercritical, but I've found that their opinions soften as the years pass.) He never published it, but put away a copy in his files. I reproduce his sketch of Stefan Bergman.

> Bergman is a small man with a mincing step, stooped over so that his head protrudes, and his short cropped black hair makes him the caricature of a little bear. He is pathetically eager to impart knowledge, of which he seems to have a good deal. His lectures are nerve-racking experiences which reduce him to a limp perspiring rag and his students to a state of somnolence, nervous itching, or amusement, depending on their constitutions. This effect is due partly to his unfamiliarity with the language, his horrible grimaces, and his peculiar accent which causes him to articulate some words with the greatest of care and quite incorrectly and to mumble other words in a jumbled hoarse whisper. Staring at the center of the board he scatters his marks at random over the outer parts.
>
> He seems an exceptionally good-hearted and well-meaning man, but one soon learns to have as little as possible to do with him, for he is so inefficient that he wastes hours mulling over the details of various arrangements, never has anything really planned in advance, and is always lacking some necessary persons or imple-ment to carry out his work. Thus, for example, when he assigned some problems, before we could start he had to have three special meetings of one hour each, in which he partially explained a very simple procedure, and when he attempted to do the problems, there was always some piece of equipment, such as thumb-tacks or a T-square, that was not to be found. His assistant, one Dr. Vaszyoni, is seldom present, and when he is his aid is of doubtful value.
>
> After about a week of lectures Bergman got down to the flow around an airfoil, where I suspect he will stay indefinitely, as he

is passionately fond of airplanes. Each day he struggles in with a six foot skeleton model of a plane, in a dilapidated state, which he triumphantly places before the class saying "Each day I bring the plane, so that you have constantly before you the idea of the plane." The model of course is of no use in illustrating his lecture, although Bergman sometime picks it up and gestures with it, as he does with erasers or chalk or paper, to illustrate particles of fluid in motion, and sometimes kicks it or steps on it a little by accident. He once asked me, as we were struggling with it together to get it around a corner and up a narrow flight of stairs, "How you like the plane?" and I was at a loss what to answer.

Thus Stefan Bergman. Was he an early version of Detective Clouzeau of *Pink Panther* fame? He was, in a number of respects.

4
Bergman at Harvard

I first met Bergman in 1948 when he was 53 and I was 25. He had a soft face, wore black-rimmed glasses, and when I first knew him he was unmarried. He was a kind man, but by no stretch of the imagination a bland man, and as a graduate student, it was only too easy to fall in with the tendencies students have of ridiculing their teachers. Have you ever heard a lecture in which the lecturer began with the word "namely"? Well, Stefan did this not infrequently and we graduate students parodied him.

I had first heard of his name in a scientific context around 1945 when I was working for NACA. I had looked at, but not completely understood, his papers on his integral operator methods applied to the theory of compressible fluids. This method depended on several complex variables, and at the time I was struggling to understand one complex variable. I had several courses in mathematics with him and after I had done all my required course work, I was employed by him "on his contract."

I was one of a constant stream of employees on his contract. Some were graduate or post-graduate students and some were "mature" mathematicians. Among the former, I recall Robert Reynolds, Henry Pollak, Geoffrey Ludford, Halsey Royden, Robert Osserman, and Lawrence Markus, all of whom were to go on to distinguished mathematical careers. Among the latter, I recall Zeev Nehari and Max Schiffer.

All Europeans seem to be polyglots and Stefan Bergman was no exception. He spoke his native Polish, and Russian, German, French, and English as well. The first three he spoke very well, and the last two quite adequately. He taught me an important lesson in communication. Sometime in the sixties I attended a mathematical conference where most of the conferees stayed at a hotel far removed from the lecture hall. As often happens, at the end of the day the conferees piled into taxis in random groups to go back to the hotel. I found myself in a cab with Bergman and André Lichnerowicz, a distinguished mathematician from France. Bergman hardly knew Lichnerowicz, and Lichnerowicz had little English at his command. Bergman immediately spoke to him in French – not very good French for even I could understand it. It occurred to me then and there that the point of language was not to be correct grammatically as was emphasized in school, but somehow to make oneself understood.

The order in terms of seniority in the Mises / Bergman group was this. At the top of the project, or contract, was Professor Richard von Mises (1883–1953) who had been, in fact, Bergman's professor at the University of Berlin. Then came Bergman. Then came the two or three "mature" mathematicians who were there on a temporary basis. And then came myself and the host of three or four graduate students. On the side was Frau Dr. Hilda Geiringer Polachek von Mises, von Mises' wife (a marriage of recent date, so it was said, for the sake of Ivy League respectability). Hilda had or would soon have a professorship of mathematics at Wheaton College, in Norton, Mass., not exactly a stone's throw from Cambridge.

Hilda had also been a student of von Mises. Rumor had it that Bergman was in love with her and wanted to marry her, but her heart was elsewhere. In the days when I used to see both of them, they were constantly talking, twenty words to the dozen. About what? Mathematics? Probably.

What was Hilda like? As my relations to her were minimal, I again call on the 1942 words of Clifford Truesdell.

> Mrs. Geiringer is a fine-looking blond woman of about forty with an unfortunately solid figure, principally in the middle parts, and a face full of European sophistication. Her lectures are said to be too difficult for her elementary students, but judging from several peeps through the crack of the door I should say she took extreme pains to make everything as clear as possible, speaking with great energy and enthusiasm. She gave the second of the colloquium lectures, which turned out to be quite an event, attended not only by all the students but also by all the mathematical faculty, a regular command performance, in fact, at the order of Dean Richardson, who was annoyed that the first in the series had been attended by no one at all. Under these circumstances it was not surprising that Mrs. Geiringer was nervous, so nervous in fact that nine-tenths of her European sophistication vanished, only the one tenth that was permanently engraved in her countenance remaining.
>
> She spoke for one and a half hours at top speed about a sort of six-dimensional vector variously called a screw, a motor, or a dynam. The subject was of interest to few, and because of her speed and her

nervous confusion, comprehensible to none except those already familiar with the subject. She wore a suit, very unbecoming to a woman of her girth, the coat of which she took off from the heat of her discourse, and after that she frequently tucked in her shirt-tail in back, like a little boy. After the lecture, during the question period she, Prager, von Mises, and Saunders Mac Lane had a slightly embarrassing discussion of something or other, mumbling softly so as hardly to be heard by the audience, which was uncertain whether to go or stay. . . .

Once there was some sort of beach party, at which Hilda wore what was then called a two-piece bathing suit, too daring for a wife but appropriate for a mistress. She had a handsome body and a lovely face. She did not seem as old as 48, but I was 23, and to a boy that age any woman over 30 seemed old. She spent most of the time talking to her friends, all male. Stefan Bergman was a dear friend of long standing, and he always talked about mathematics; I doubt he even noticed that any woman had a body. Unfortunately Hilda's lectures were exceeding dull. Dynams or whatever they are called were already just superfluous baggage.

[Note for future biographers of science. In the years that followed, Truesdell had a considerable correspondence with Geiringer. Many of his letters can be found in the Geiringer deposit in the Harvard rare book library.]

5
Working for Bergman

I recall that when I was first hired by Bergman, I had to go to von Mises for approval. I had known of von Mises through my undergraduate reading of his treatise *Probability, Statistics, and Truth*, and later, while I was at the NACA, as the author of a very fine book on the dynamics of airplane flight. (Mises had been a pilot in the Austrian Air Force in World War I.)

Mises was my first, and I think my only, direct encounter with what Americans call the "Herr Doktor Professor" manner: I could feel it immediately on stepping into his office. His bookcases were filled not only with contemporary scientific literature, but with early editions of Newton; that sort of thing. And filled also (so I was told later) with first editions of the poet Rilke. Here was a cultured and refined man. But the man's hauteur was so thick it could have been cut with a knife.

I trembled. I wanted the job. Mises asked me the title of my doctoral thesis. I told him. He immediately rephrased the title in a way that told me he knew what it was all about, if not in detail, then in principle. I trembled further lest the Great Man think that I had wasted my time on trivialities. I nodded at his reformulation. The interview was over. I was hired. Though I used to see him regularly tiptoeing down the hall lightly, and at seminars, this was my only encounter with him.

Mises was too old to have adopted the relaxed American professorial manner. Bergman, on the other hand, was not. He was a paragon of informality. Of course, while Mises was alive, Bergman lived in the shadow of his professor. Later, he lived in the shadow of his own eccentricities. He was modest, but it was a modesty thoroughly infused and flavored by the monomania of his own scientific accomplishments.

Bergman had developed a number of major mathematical ideas: the kernel function, a certain kind of integral operator, and the distinguished boundary of regions in the space of two complex variables. I enjoyed his lectures, learned much from them, and wrote a few things myself on the first two topics. I considered Bergman's kernel function as having high aesthetic appeal and I couldn't let it go for a number of years.

With these three arrows in his scientific quiver, Bergman roamed the scientific world and, like Cupid, would shoot one of the three at random into whomever he perceived would not speed away from him at high velocity. The number of apocryphal stories mounted in which he confronted bus drivers, waitresses, with the words, "This, my distinguished boundary. Shall I explain you?"

He drew figures galore on the back of envelopes. He had models constructed of four-dimensional objects that played a role in his theory, often a series of three-dimensional "stills" with time as the fourth dimension. Indeed, I probably owed my job at the National Bureau of Standards in Washington to the fact that Joseph Hilsenrath of the Bureau was constructing such models for him at the time.

He drew pictures in a day in which such activity was considered by mathematical analysts to be almost declassé. Bergman would have been absolutely delighted with the incredibly high level animated computer graphics now available, and he would most certainly have been able to derive theoretic inspiration from them.

He told me that there were two kinds of mathematical intuition: the algebraic and the geometric, and that the work of Weierstrass and Riemann, two great 19th century mathematicians, stood as paradigms; the former of the algebraic and the latter of the geometric. He assigned to himself the geometric or Riemannian intuition.

He was constantly worried about his scientific reputation, and his worries often expressed themselves along competitive lines. "Is my work of the same quality as X's?" He would ask his graduate students or post-docs this question, although they were hardly in a position to answer it with their own judgements. If they answered him at all, it would have been merely to repeat the gossip of the graduate school community.

Working for Bergman was not easy for me. The reason, I think, was that I never knew what he wanted of me. Did he want me to work by myself along the lines of his own interests? He never set a specific problem for me to solve. Did he want to do joint work with me as junior partner? Did he want me to correct the English in his technical papers and in the books he wrote? Did he want simply to use me as a sounding board? One of his favorite expressions was, "You understand what it is I tell you?"

I did all of the above, but never really found out what, deep down, he wanted. Perhaps he really wanted nothing of me and I was only a young and deserving post-doc that the U.S. Government was subsidizing through his grace. That grace extended generously to all the young people that worked for him.

In the wake of the GI Bill and of the growing cold war competition between the United States and the Soviet Union, many, many new university jobs were created in the early fifties. Bergman left MIT in 1952 for a professorship at Stanford. His days of wandering were over. He was Professor from 1952–1974 and, thereafter, Professor Emeritus till his death in 1977.

From 1952 on, busy with my own work at the Bureau of Standards, and with a growing family, I lost track of Bergman's work, of his graduate and thesis students, and the state of his government contracts. He would phone me long distance from time to time and send me reprints. I would meet him at conferences and have coffee with him and Edie.

6
The True Meaning of Exile

Emigration is hard from the purely personal standpoint: people generally think of the pain of nostalgia; but what is worse is the pain of estrangement: the process whereby what was intimate becomes foreign.

— Milan Kundera, *Testaments Betrayed*

In my correspondence with Professor Truesdell, he added the following to the material in the old student letter to his grandmother:

In later years Hilda Geiringer told my wife and me a story about Bergman. When all America had come to call everybody Bill and Jane, he asked her if he could speak to her alone in complete secrecy. She agreed. He said: "I know that now in public we have to be Hilda and Stefan, but when we are alone together, may I still call you Frau Dr. Geiringer and will you call me Herr Dr. Bergman?"

This story epitomizes for me the pain and the suffering of exile. "How can we sing the Lord's songs in a strange land?"
And yet we do.

Stefan Bergman c. 1952 at MIT

IV

The Rothschild
I Knew

Spune - mi tot; începe dela bonjour!

Tell me everything. Begin when he said "bonjour"!

— Marguerite Dorian

1
Symplocarpus Foetidus and Its Aftermath

One cannot start with Adam and Eve, or with the Big Bang. Nevertheless, I must start "the history of my friendship with Rothschild" before the *bonjour*. So let me start somewhere in between, in the spring of 1939. I will start with a confession. In those months I was a senior in high school, and I was asked to write a final composition for my English class. The spring was beautiful, and I used to walk my dog along the banks of the Merrimack selecting always the path through the woods that, as legend had it, the Indians used to take on their treks to the Winnepesaukee region.

The first signs of spring along this path are the young skunk cabbages poking their green spathes up through the wet earth. For my essay, I chose to elaborate the proposition that the United States (which had no national flower) ought to nominate the skunk cabbage as such. The thesis was my own, and I was serious about it. I defended it on the following grounds. First, that Benjamin Franklin had suggested the turkey as our national bird, and so the rudeness or the vulgarity of my selection had a basis in American tradition. Second, that this so-called cabbage (*symplocarpus foetidus*) was hardy, widespread (particularly along the marshy banks of the Merrimack), and since it put forth marvelously green shoots when the snow was still on the ground, was a harbinger of spring and therefore of the renewal of spirits that spring implied. As regards the odor that endows the plant with its name, well, that could be given the positive interpretation of cranky independence. A "Don't Tread on Me" sort of thing, and therefore very American indeed.

The mind that created this thesis should really have concentrated more on Shelley or Burns; should have learned who Yeats or Ernest Hemingway were and learned to write glibly about those gentlemen. Nonetheless, despite the discomfiture of my English teacher who thought that in parody I was reducing her best teaching efforts to dust and ashes, despite miserable grades on my English college board exams, I got into Harvard, the college of my first choice. I suppose it helped that I went off the scale in mathematics.

English A was mandated; that was inevitable. After a most awful first semester, my section man perceived that I did not have the makings of a literary critic, and he was wise enough to perceive that there was really no need whatever for me to become one. The world did not require it. He encouraged to go my own route. That encouragement caused my rude cabbage to blossom, so to speak. The man's name was William Murphy, and God rewarded him in later years by having him inherit the residuary papers of Jack Yeats (the poet's father), and by allowing him to write a most substantial biography of that eccentric Irish father.

One afternoon in the Fall of 1940, Albert Guerard Jr., who taught my section of English A-1 (the next higher course in composition and taken optionally, I'll have you know), bought me a cup of coffee in the Harvard Square Diner on Massachusetts Avenue adjacent to the Yard. I had just had a conference with him in his office, discussing a story I had written, and he had invited me for coffee. Guerard was then all of twenty six, bilingual and debonair, but already a novelist, a critic, and a world authority on Joseph Conrad and Thomas Hardy. I, quite au contraire, was a green sophomore of seventeen, passionately in love with the short story, both in its specific instances as well as an abstract object of Platonic contemplation.

My college work was going well that year, and the ten minutes Guerard and I sat side by side at the counter were as close as I have ever come in my life to breathing stardust: in this case, the stardust of authorship. Many of my generation were affected similarly. I began to think along the lines of "Guerard & I," or "We authors," as Disraeli once wrote to Queen Victoria. The individual twinkles of that stardust have now been obliterated, and my memory retains only one feature of that conversation almost a half century ago.

"Read Elizabeth Bowen's *The Death of the Heart*," Guerard said to me as we took leave. I nodded assent. It took me twenty years to get to the book. And when I did, I found its vague, misty, ambiguous Anglo-Irish atmosphere not to my liking. So much for assignments turned in late.

I read stories by the basketful. I read the old volumes of *Best Short Stories* edited annually by Edward O'Brien. By hanging around the second hand book stores of Third Avenue in Manhattan, I collected out-of-print, hard to get copies of *Story Magazine*, edited in those days by Whit Burnett and Martha Foley. I tried Joseph Conrad and hated him. His metaphysics were not mine. I tried Thomas Hardy and loved him, and I wound up reading a shelffull (or two) of Hardy before I became a Junior.

Through my short story interests I met a classmate who was also wrapped up in short story writing: Norman Mailer. Our rooms were close by. We became friends immediately, a friendship that lasted some fifteen years but became increasingly attenuated by our entering different worlds: he, the world of literature, and I the world of mathematics. In some ways Mailer was responsible for my realization that my long suit was mathematics and not writing. Mailer was in a parallel section of English A-1, having already produced two novels and a handful of stories in high school. For me, each sentence I wrote was a matter of sweating blood. I wanted to do it and I did it, but it did not come easily. In contrast, mathematics came very easily. Later, when I had to pit my understanding and intuition against those of the great mathematicians of previous ages and of mathematical contemporaries of world renown, the subject became much much harder. When an understanding came of the limits of my own abilities, this added another dimension to the difficulties.

The war came, and I was drafted into the Air Force. I was sent, on reserve status, to Langley Field, Virginia. I spent three years as an aerodynamicist. I wrote my first scientific paper at Langley Field, and out of this experience came a deepened understanding of applied mathematics and of theories of scientific computation. These subjects formed the basis of my professional career.

For a while I lived in a trailer camp in Newport News, Virginia, about an hour by bus from Langley Field or two hours by bus and ferry from the great naval base at Norfolk. To get home, I had to change buses in downtown Newport News. At the transfer point there was a large magazine stand, almost invariably tended by a young man of sixteen or so. I would stop and pick up material to bring back to my trailer-dorm. As the weeks went on, I got to talking to this news attendant. About school. About writing. About the short story. The shipyards in Newport News were alive with construction workers. Sailors, soldiers, fliers, sweethearts were everywhere. Italian prisoners of war wearing POW armbands roamed the streets under mild surveillance. Newport News was alive in some respects, but it was also a part of what H.L. Mencken in the 1920's called the Desert of the Beaux Arts.

My new friend (I never knew his name nor he mine) came from the mountains of Virginia. He lived with his aunt in the city to enable him to go to a better sort of school. For several months I met him regularly and "lectured" to him about the short story, playing Al Guerard to his Phil Davis. He was so green, I thought; so green. (I was then all of twenty-one.) I threw stardust in his eyes, and he reacted nicely. I wanted to get him to go to college. But in those days, the future hardly existed for any young person. Time had stopped. Time was on hold. He knew that he would be drafted shortly.

The summer came, and my wife, Hadassah (we had been married in January), joined me in my trailer camp. This was the turning point of the war; there were now substantial Allied victories. The Italian prisoner of war camp a few yards beyond our trailer seemed unusually full of men. High school was over for my newsie and he disappeared into the army. I should like to think that his name was William Styron, who came from Newport News and made a great reputation as a novelist in the early postwar years. But such a coincidence would be very unlikely.

Mailer, also, was drafted into the army, and was sent to the Pacific theater. Out of his experience came *The Naked and the Dead* and subsequent fame. We corresponded, even while he was posted to the Philippines, and later through the mid-fifties. Inevitably, as my mathematical concerns occupied most of my professional thought, this correspondence eased off. Then it came to a halt. And far as writing short stories or anything else was concerned, I was left only with a vague hankering to write and a very pale residue of the stardust of ten years before.

In the late 1950's, while I was working at the National Bureau of Standards in Washington, the hankering translated itself into a more active desire. I began to see how I could combine words and mathematics in a more literary way than is necessary for professional paper-writing. I projected forward to a time when I might write a series of books, some deeply professional and technical, some popular, and some philosophical.

In 1963, I moved from Washington to Brown University to the Division of Applied Mathematics. I found a milieu that regarded the writing projects I had already begun with some approval; well, if not with active approval, at least with no active disapproval. In the years that followed, my writing at different levels, professional, popular, philosophical, was well received by each respective mathematical audience. Quite naturally this was a source of satisfaction, and despite thoughts that I was betraying – or at the very least diluting – the world of theory with the world of rhetoric, despite thoughts that I was forsaking the production of new mathematics for the interpretation of what had been already created, I took my success as a message to give in to that old hankering and to go on with my writing.

2
Fan Mail

In the early sixties, I did a series of articles on mathematical topics for *Science World*, a magazine for high school students. The following year, Bill Chinn, a San Francisco mathematician, continued this series. Still later we collected some of these articles, polished them up a bit, and Simon & Schuster put them out as a trade publication under the title *3.1416 and All That*. The number 3.1416, well known to all scientists and usually abbreviated as the Greek letter pi, is the ratio of the length of the circumference of a circle to its diameter.

As the number of popular (or semi-popular) books I had written mounted, a trickle of "fan" mail began to flow into my office. I put the word in quotes because the letters I received were only occasionally complimentary. Generally, such letters found fault with a comma that I had misplaced, a phrase that was misinterpretable, a name I had misspelled, a date that was off by a few days, or, once in a great while, a damn fool error I had made.

One such letter I received – this was about twenty-five years ago – complained about my transliteration of a Russian name. I took my revenge. I wrote a small book called *The Thread*, which poked fun at the nigglers' mindset. Of course, in its turn, and I had not anticipated it, *The Thread* provoked a new generation of letters of its own, kindly pointing out new errata and filling in crevasses of detail that my correspondent was most certain I would want to have. On the plus side, one reviewer in Poland pointed out that I had created a new school of literary endeavor that might with some justice be called "tangentialism."

Shortly after *3.1416 and All That* appeared, I received this piece of fan mail:

> Dear Professor Davis:
>
> I have been reading your book and I think there is a grievous fault in your title. [I remember the word 'grievous' distinctly. My fan must have been reading Marc Antony's speech: "it was a grievous fault and grievously hath Caesar answered it."] You must be aware, surely, that the value of π is not 3.1416, but is 3.1415926535. I should like to suggest that in the next printing of your book, and in the interests of scientific accuracy, you change its title to *3.1415926535 and All That*. Better still, please omit the words "and all that," which I find rather flippant.
>
> Yours sincerely,
> Caswell Wildhaker

I answered this letter:

> Dear Mr. Wildhaker:
>
> Many thanks, indeed, for your incisive remarks about my title. In preparation for the Vermehrte und Verbesserte Auflage, Dr. Chinn & I will seriously consider altering the title to *3.1515926535 and All That*. Actually, your suggestion will appeal greatly to Dr. Chinn, who is a man known for his great punctilio,

and who originally proposed *3.14159265358979323846 and All That* as a title.

Yours very truly,
P.J.D.

One of the nice things about having a coauthor is not only does he do half the work – well, hopefully – but, more importantly, you can hide behind him whenever the need arises. You can lay the blame for all your mistakes on his shoulder and you can take credit for all his virtues.

The improved and enlarged edition did not hit the newsstands for many years, as will become clear shortly. By the time it did (1985), the value of π was known to more than four million decimals, and even later to billions of decimals, and these would have crowded the front cover rather a bit.

Letters containing errata, on the whole, are sent in a friendly, helpful spirit. After all, you, as author, would surely want to get things right when you come to put out your enlarged and improved edition. Alas, as regards deeply professional books, where a lifetime sales of 1,000 copies can be considered *un succés fou*, the enlarged and improved editions very seldom see the light of day.

Less friendly is the crank mail. This mail generally implies: now that you've published your book, you may think you are so great and so smart. But I too am great and smart, and I have solved most of the unsolved problems of the world, from squaring the circle and perpetual motion to world peace. I have started my own desktop foundation to promulgate my ideas, and I call it the Metalevel Foundation. I have enclosed pamphlets J-1234 and K-5678 that I wrote myself. And I want you to read them and admit that I am great also.

I generally ignore such mail. Painful experience has taught me that a degree of callousness is necessary for survival. Occasionally, of course, I would receive a letter to which I could react in a positive way, but such letters were rare.

3
The Distribution of the Prime Numbers

One afternoon in January 1986, the secretary of my department called me and said that I had received a package and didn't I want to come down for it. I was in the middle of something and I answered her that it could wait. I'd pick the package up on my way home.

"I think it might be important," she answered back, "it was delivered by courier."

"By courier? What's courier these days? You mean special delivery? Priority mail? Federal Express?"

"No. Courier. Come down. You'll see."

Downstairs, I found a large, slim plastic package waiting, pasted over with shipping marks and stamps from Logan International Airport in Boston, and Heathrow in London, and marked overall "Worldwide Courier Express." The return address was given as N.M. Rothschild & Sons, Ltd., The City, London, EC4P 4DU, and it was clear that it had been sent off late the previous afternoon. This indeed was a package worth coming downstairs for, if only to have confirmed before my eyes that despite execrable mail delivery service these days, with physical mail humiliated by the electronic mail received on a computer terminal, it was still possible to get something delivered rapidly if only you were willing to pay enough.

But for what reason on earth would N.M. Rothschild & Sons, The City, London want to communicate with me in such an expensive way? There are times when I rush madly to open up a letter or a package, often tearing the contents as I do; at other times, I like to delay the process so as to enhance the pleasure. This was one of the former occasions. Before I tore it open I tried to guess what it might contain, just as one often does on receiving a birthday present.

The only thing I could imagine was GOLD. I knew that Rothschild's Bank in London was one of the principal gold dealers in the world. Gold was touted by many as an inflation hedge and was being bought by many people of modest means. Obviously, Rothschild's Bank had got my name off a computerized mailing list that had me coded (wrongfully) as a very up-market prospect and was trying to sell me gold. I thought that I might as well chuck the thing out without even opening it, like I do with those envelopes that read in large type "MR. DAVIS: YOU MAY HAVE ALREADY WON $1,000,000."

If I had chucked the package, I would have no story to tell. On the basis of a misinterpretation I would have missed an adventure. In mathematics this phenomenon is known as "instability with respect to initial conditions," and has led to deep and paradoxical theories that assert that the universe is both determined and chaotic simultaneously.

The package contained a letter. The letter was typewritten on heavy bond, embossed with a London home address, and went along the following lines (I seem to have misplaced the original):

Dear Professor Davis:

May I refer to your book *3.1416 and all That?* On page . . . of your book, you have a diagram which relates to the distribution of the prime numbers. I believe that there has been a mislabelling of one of the axes, or possibly a miscomputation. I believe it should be.... I wonder whether you would agree with me? Please do let me know.

[Signed]   V. Rothschild

[Typed]   Lord Rothschild

The letter was signed with a fine pen in rather small and delicate handwriting.

Another "fan" letter of the usual type? A small error of mine, I supposed, had triggered it. But this particular communication could hardly be considered run-of-the-mill. One does not get letters every day of the week from someone claiming to be Lord Rothschild and delivered by courier. And on mathematics, mind you. A hoax possibly? The English are more given to practical jokes than Americans. What friend or fiend in London would send me such a thing? Clearly, this letter would require careful consideration. All unknown correspondents are *a priori* equal, but some are more equal.

No gold! No condominium deals with free gifts if I showed up on Jekyll's Island, Georgia! No clever come-ons involving the Isle of Sark in the English Channel where the tax laws are liberal. Here instead was a bona fide inquiry about a fairly elementary (to a professional, that is) piece of mathematics from a man who I assumed was the head of the House of Rothschild in London. I went to my shelf and got down a copy of *3.1416 and All That*. It had only recently been reprinted. I opened it to page.... I found I had indeed made a slight error. Lord Rothschild was right!

In addition to the hair-splitters, there are a certain number of mathematical crazies in the world who plague the professionals by inundating them with incorrect or incomprehensible material. It is not always an easy matter to distinguish what is correct from what is incorrect, to distinguish what is new, imaginative, and promising from what is absolutely crackpot. Philosophers of the history of science have chewed over this point long and inconclusively. Most professionals deal with submissions of "amateur" material quite curtly. They have to, or else they would never get their own work done. If, in the process, some pearls get overlooked or discarded, well, that's just tough.

Yes, tough. The world exists mainly as a potentiality. Not everything that might come forward does come forward. One can imagine a myriad of alternate human worlds built upon one and the same Planet Earth. One can imagine a myriad of alternate personal lives built upon one and the same physical frame. One often says, if I (or my parents) had done thus and so in 1957, how different my life would now be. Potential Beethovens, Tolstoys, Abraham Lincolns are always emerging and being snuffed out. Many a flower is born to blush unseen. So, with a slight sigh and a light flip, one tosses the material into the wastebasket. At least, that's what I do.

In addition to the hair-splitters and the crazies, there are also a certain number of people, generally retired engineers or the like, who, with a modest background in mathematics, pursue the subject as a hobby for their own amusement. They pursue it intelligently, but often unimaginatively, and they do not realize the extent to which the answers to certain questions are already known. The existence of the personal computer has greatly widened the range of interesting things that the amateur can now undertake if given proper guidance. Such amateurs sometimes write to a professional; but again, although we are dealing here with a different category of individual than the crazies, such people also get short shrift from professionals. Professionals, by very definition, are busy people.

On the assumption that the letter from Lord Rothschild was not a hoax, I concluded that he was in the amateur category, and I proposed to answer his inquiry on that basis.

4
A Letter Gets Answered

In 1984, Klaus Peters, my editor, then with the Swiss publisher Birkhäuser, happened to run across a copy of *3.1416 and All That*, which was then long out of print. Peters, who is one of the great optimists in the world, decided that he would like to revive the book and bring out a paperback edition. Simon & Schuster, the original publisher, was willing. My coauthor William Chinn was willing. I could see no harm in it, so the thing was done.

On the whole, I find revising published material quite distasteful. As I reread, I imagine so many better ways of saying the same things. I am aware of new material that would cast much brighter light. The only honest way to proceed would be to junk the whole manuscript and begin again. Neither Chinn nor I wanted to do that.

We did a very superficial cleanup job, and I added a couple of pages having to do with some exciting theoretical developments on the high precision computation (i.e., millions of decimal places) of the number pi. After all, pi was in the title of the book – inaccurately, as Caswell Wildhaker informed me – and I wanted to make a nod in its direction. We submitted these few changes, the presses rolled, and one copy of *3.1416 and All That* somehow reached Lord Rothschild in England.

A day after the arrival of the courier letter – I still had not answered it – Peters called me up.

"I don't know how many copies of the book you've sold," I said to him, "but I know where one copy is. It's in the hands of Lord Rothschild in England. Now how about that?"

"You mean the Rothschild of Chateau Lafitte Rothschild wine? The Rothschild of Soufflé Rothschild?"

"Same family, if you go back to the late seventeen hundreds. Different branch. Wine is the French branch. Mine is the English branch."

I read the letter to him.

"Are you going to answer him?"

"Are you crazy? Of course I'm going to answer him."

"Great. And when you do, ask him for a plug for your book. We'll run it on the next printing."

"If there is a next printing."

The vagueness that I felt when pressed with regard to the precise identity of Lord Rothschild sent me to the reference shelves. In any case, I would have consulted *Who's Who* or Debrett's *Peerage* prior to answering, for I was pretty vague myself about the man with whom I was dealing.

Rothschild. Who is Rothschild? What do you mean who is Rothschild? Rothschild is Rothschild, that's who Rothschild is.

To someone who is Jewish, Rothschild is the archetypical, paradigmatic Jewish millionaire: wealthy beyond the dreams of avarice; powerful, his word hearkened to by every Throne (in the days when there were thrones) and every Foreign Office and every Treasury; philanthropic; hobnobbing and intermarried with European aristocracy. Rothschild is a dynasty: several dynasties. Rothschild is a myth. Rothschild is a legend. It matters not that there are many Rothschilds spread out in space over the world and in time over seven or eight generations. There always is and always will be a Rothschild. Rothschild is a Platonic concept, an abstraction, existing in the mind of every Jew who is aware of the larger world. Rothschild is the actor George Arliss playing Rothschild in

The House of Rothschild, an early movie. Rothschild is a Broadway musical. Rothschild is Soufflé Rothschild, Chateau Lafitte Rothschild.

Rothschild is also real. Alive. Flesh and blood. Doing things. Reading *3.1416 and All That*, for example.

"If I were Rothschild, I would be richer than Rothschild," goes the old Yiddish joke.

"How would that be possible?"

"Well, I'd do a little teaching on the side."

Or a little shoemaking, or a little tailoring, depending upon who tells the story.

Did it much matter who Rothschild is *specifically*? It did not. Rothschild is a symbol, an imago, an ikon. Rothschild is part of one's language. The word "Rothschild" has deep semantic and semiotic content.

I recall saying to my wife when I got home from the university that day, "You know that today I'm richer than Rothschild."

"How is that?"

"Well, I got a letter from Lord Rothschild and I suppose that he doesn't often write to himself."

Still, one doesn't write a letter to a symbol or explain something to a soufflé. One writes to a person, flesh and blood, a person who lives in a house at a specific address, a person who has two hands and ten fingers just as you or I do, and who also has a head and a heart. It was difficult, though, to shake off the feeling that I was about to write a letter to an abstraction.

5
I Lose a Legend and Gain a Lord

I do not keep copies of the letters I write. Well – with one exception: if I write a letter that has to do with money, I try to keep a copy of it for a while. Now that I work on a word processor, I try to keep its disc clear of old correspondence. I wonder how the word processor is going to alter the work of future biographers. Thank God that the word processor is killing the industry of putting out editions of Carlyle's *Essay on Burns* with all of Carlyle's corrections and additions. Something is surely lost, and I am not weeping.

On the other hand, I tend to keep the letters I receive for about five years. Then I throw them out in huge batches. I shall have to simulate my letters to Lord Rothschild, but I will be able to quote verbatim a number that he sent me.

Late January, 1986

Dear Lord Rothschild:

You are right. There is an error in the diagram on page.... However, it is very slight. It should have read as follows: ....

The theory of prime numbers is one of the most fascinating in the whole of mathematics. It contains some of the most difficult material in mathematics and at the same time many of its statements are easily accessible to the tyro.

You might enjoy reading a clip from a more recent book of mine, *The Mathematical Experience*, which alludes to the same sphere of ideas. [Xerox enclosed.]

I should be very glad to hear of your mathematical interests.

Yours sincerely,

PJD

I sent this letter off by regular airmail. A very interesting fish indeed had swum up my stream. My old hankering to write, to tell stories, surfaced again; perhaps there would be something here that would be worth the telling, and the last line of my letter was a clear attempt to lift Rothschild's letter out of the category of routine inquiries. You cannot catch fish unless you let down a hook.

While waiting for an answer (if indeed there would be an answer), I consulted *Who's Who in Britain* and the *Dictionary of National Biography* in order to get some sort of a picture of my correspondent. Nathaniel Mayer Victor Rothschild, Third Baron Rothschild, was born in 1910. His title was inherited from his uncle, Lionel Walter Rothschild (1868–1937), an eminent zoologist who died unmarried.

Victor (as he called himself) Rothschild went to Harrow, took a degree at Trinity College, Cambridge, was a biologist specializing in the microchemistry of fertilization, a member of the Royal Society (the British scientific élite), and for a number of years was Director of Research at Royal Dutch Shell. He was also Chairman of the Board of N.M. Rothschild & Sons (Nathan Mayer Rothschild, 1777–1836, founder of the English branch of the family), Chairman of Biotechnology Investments, past director of BOAC and many other companies. He wrote a good half dozen books and won many awards, including two in the military line: the George Medal and the medal of the American Legion of Merit.

The list of his achievements goes on and on. If one consults Debrett one finds much more, including the family coat of arms with its lion and unicorn, shields, quarterings, coronets, supporters and motto all precisely described in the arcane and algorithmic language of heraldry.

"My goodness," I thought, as I read these things. "This man has everything: money, genealogy, position, brains, high regard, honors, children. He must be the happiest man alive. And now that he is retired from active research and administration, he pursues mathematics as a hobby. This should make him even happier."

In about two weeks I had a reply. Like the first letter, it was sent from N.M. Rothschild & Sons, but typed on personal stationery from his home near St. James Park.

6th February 1986

Dear Professor Davis:

   Thank you so much for answering my letter and for the photostat of part of *The Mathematical Experience* which I enjoyed reading. In such an innocent account I was a little surprised to see the equation for $R(n)$ on p. 214 which is much too difficult for me as I believe there is some complex variable theory hidden in it.

   I am not a professional mathematician – nor an amateur one for that matter – but for various reasons I became interested in primes particularly because of the remark in Hardy and Wright, "we know that the primes near x thin out (in some vague sense) as x increases."

   "Vague" stimulated me to have a look at the primes (like thousands of others). I came to the conclusion that they thin out in a *vague* way if you look at their distribution "microscopically" in contradistinction to "macroscopically." I thought it would be interesting to plot $\pi(x)/\delta x$, see the enclosed curve in which the interval δx is $6\sqrt{x}$.

   [There followed several more paragraphs which explained the graph that was enclosed.]

[Signed]   Rothschild
[Typed]   Lord Rothschild

What was this mathematics all about? The story, briefly, is this. Most numbers can be split into factors. For example, $14 = 7 \times 2$, $16 = 2 \times 2 \times 2 \times 2$, $18 = 2 \times 3 \times 3$. However, some numbers, such as 11, 13, or 41, cannot be split in this manner. A number that cannot be split is called a prime mumber. The mathematicians of classical antiquity knew that there is an unlimited number of prime numbers. But the prime numbers are very strange things.

They occur in a rather irregular manner and there is no easy or transparent way of telling beforehand just where they will occur.

Now what Rothschild observed, and it had been observed since at least the middle of the 1700's, was this: if one focuses not on the individual prime numbers (the microscopic), but on the macroscopic, the prime numbers in aggregate, i.e., the number of primes up to a given large number n, then this aggregate follows a law that is very simple. The phenomenon is summarized in what is called the *Prime Number Theorem*, and this theorem constitutes one of the jewels of the Theory of Numbers.

The Prime Number Theorem is itself very simple to state, but its demonstration is beyond the grasp of the average mathematical amateur. The explication of the further subtleties of the distribution of prime numbers would involve even the professional in a theory of incredible depth and difficulty.

I myself had never worked professionally in this area. However, when I was in graduate school, I took several courses in analytic number theory, covering the work of Landau, Hardy, Littlewood, and van der Corput, the middle two being Great Men on the Cambridge, England, mathematical scene, and so I was familiar with the basic methodology.

These, then, were the ideas that Rothschild was playing around with, not as a professional, not as an amateur – he himself denied this status – but for a variety of reasons which he did not care to elaborate.

Just what was his status vis-a-vis mathematics? We shall soon see. After I received his first letter, I treated him as a rank amateur. After the second letter, it was clear that this was a bad error. In replying to the second letter, I raised the level of mathematical sophistication of my correspondence, put in a few quips and personal touches, and sent it off by regular air mail.

In two weeks' time, I received an answer, also by courier, but this time typed on stationery with a home address in Cambridge (England, of course; not Massachusetts). The letter was quite freewheeling in throwing around mathematical ideas. The tone was quite cordial.

It so happened that Hadassah and I had planned to visit Cambridge University in May–June of that year, partly to visit Sue Wesley, a friend who lives in Cambridge, and partly to give a lecture in the Department of Applied Mathematics and Theoretical Physics, but mostly for fun and relaxation. I recall saying to Hadassah that if I now played my cards right, we would soon receive an invitation to sherry with Lord Rothschild.

The invitation was dated 28 February, 1986:

Dear Professor Davis,

   Thank you for your letter.   I don't want to put you to the trouble of looking up references, if only because I have got Riesel, H. (1985) Prime Numbers and Computer Methods for Factorization, Birkhauser.   God knows there are enough references in it.

   Would you care to come and have a sherry (or a bourbon on the rocks if you prefer it) around 6.00 p.m. on Thursday, May 22?   Or, if you are still here, at the same time on Friday, May 23?   It would be a great pleasure to meet you.

Yours,
Rothschild

Lord Rothschild

No, I haven't yet got a personal computer but my associate, mentioned above, has green computer fingers and, believe it or not, access to a Cray.

Attached were directions to his home in Cambridge, and the passage,

> I wonder if your first-year students have looked at Rothschild V. & Logothetis N. (1986), *Probability Distributions*, John Wiley & Sons. I think it may fill a gap. . . .

Well, there it was, laid out on the table. First, the invitation. Obviously, I had played my cards right. Second, his status. Professional mathematician? Certainly not. Amateur mathematician? No way! The man had written (or coauthored) a book on the theory of probability. Rothschild was somewhere betwixt and between.

A question then arose in my mind. In view of the facts that Rothschild had considerable mathematical experience, that he lived a fifteen-minute walk away from one of the most high-powered mathematical faculties in the entire world, that he had coauthored a book on probability, why on earth did he initiate a correspondence with me, at a distance of three thousand miles, over a trivial, easily corrected error, and then continue this correspondence at the level of a math buff?

I have had considerable experience with people who write me with niggling complaints. I thought I recognized their style and knew what made them tick. My initial correspondence with Rothschild convinced me that he was not in this category, but as subsequent letters showed, he was not above and did enjoy correcting the little mistakes of others. Was this the sum and substance of his initiating the correspondence? I thought not. All in all, though, Rothschild was hard to classify. He was a *hapax legomenon*, unique, one of a kind. So are we all, but Rothschild is more unique because Rothschild is also a Rothschild.

6
I Lose a Lord – Well, Sort of – and Gain a Man

Our correspondence continued throughout the spring of 1986.

12th March 1986

Dear Professor Davis:

I did not notice in my letter to you of February 28 my secretary had put "Lord Rothschild" under where I signed. I tend not to use this designation in the U.S. because "Lord" is thought to be either an eccentric Christian name (cf. Duke Ellington) or an anachronism.

I think I am too convex to attend your lecture. [I had invited him to attend my Cambridge lecture which was titled "The Approximation of Convex Sets."]

[There follows a discussion of the love-hate relationship that exists between authors and their publishers; I was then in the middle of some publishing negotiations and had told Rothschild about them. He responded with his own stories. He had written at least ten books, the most technical of which was his book on fertilization.]

[Signed] Yrs.

Victor Rothschild

In the middle of May, 1986 my wife and I checked into the Bon Sejour Bed & Breakfast, Tenison Road, Cambridge, about halfway between the railroad station and the university. It was a five-minute walk to our friend Sue's apartment and a fifteen-minute walk to the Applied Mathematics Department where my friend Professor Michael Powell held forth. Our room was just barely adequate, but it came with private bathroom facilities (en suite, as they say in the UK) which, again, were just barely adequate. There was a TV in the room but no phone. I recall watching the bloody football riots in Belgium.

Every morning at eight we marched dutifully into the small breakfast area downstairs, where a half-dozen tables had been set up. Like death and taxation, the breakfast menu was one of the stable things at the Bon Sejour: tea, coffee, Weetabix, toast, and jam. This was the abbreviated breakfast. If we opted for the "full English breakfast," bacon, sausage, eggs, tinned tomatoes and mushrooms would be added. These were served in silence by an old handyman-waiter who resembled Bela Lugosi, wore a rubber apron, and, I was sure, had stayed on at the Bon Sejour through at least six changes of ownership and management.

I should like to add here an encomium for breakfast. I would argue that breakfast is (or can be) the most exciting meal of the day. The blood is rising, and expectations are high. Yesterday's disappointments are put aside, and there is little need for polite conversation. One is allowed, without jeopardizing self-esteem or social status, to be somewhat rude at breakfast, somewhat private. And when a retreat behind a newspaper or behind a wall of sleepy introspection is combined with the self-renewal implicit in a dish of something pungent, like huevos rancheros or fried lox and onions, it can do much to carry one forward for a few hours. Such exotic fare was not available at the Bon Sejour at £12 per person per day. Alas. Cold tinned mushrooms and Weetabix, and then out into the wet drizzle known as British Summer.

The Bon Sejour was well removed from Tourist Cambridge, and its clientèle was a salad bar of English types. We met one American, though, a man who taught at the University of Alaska in Fairbanks and was visiting the Polar Institute at Cambridge. We met families from the Midlands bringing their children to visit their grandparents. We met groups of itinerant electricians who moved from job to job living in B and B's. "Foine lads," said the cook/owner as she came out of the kitchen and tried to unload a few more cold mushrooms onto my plate.

The day approached for afternoon sherry with Lord Rothschild. I thought I had better ring him up, announce I was in Cambridge, and confirm the date. Another thing: I wanted to bring my wife along. My original negotiations for sherry had been phrased in terms of myself alone.

My mental processes began now to reverse themselves. The man himself was replaced by the Lord, and the Lord, in turn, was replaced by the Abstraction. How on earth does one make a phone call to an abstraction? Can a poet call up Erato, the Muse of Poetry, or a historian call up and consult the Zeitgeist?

How then does one call up Lord Rothschild? The answer is simple enough. The same way that one calls up for airline information or calls up one's cousin Teddy. I went down to the coinbox in the front hall of the Bon Sejour and dialed the unlisted number. His Lordship's secretary answered, a cheerful voice. I told her who I was and what I wanted.

She answered, "Oh yes, Professor Davis. Lord Rothschild is expecting you for sherry on the 22nd."

So far, so good. They know me. I put in the request on behalf of Hadassah.

The secretary answered, "Lord Rothschild is in Switzerland. I'll ring him about it. Where can I reach you with his answer?"

Where indeed could she ring me back? At the coinbox in the front hall of a minus-three-star Bed & Breakfast? Could I trust old Bela Lugosi to answer the phone, take the message, come upstairs and deliver it without garbling it? I could not. I was embarrassed. But sanity and resource prevailed, and I gave her Sue's number. Sue is paraplegic and most always near her phone.

Within the half-hour the handyman shuffled up to our bedroom door with a message: call this number (Sue's). I called Sue and she reported to me that Lord Rothschild's secretary had called and would I most certainly bring Mrs. Davis for sherry.

Sue was thrilled, actually, by her unexpected phone call and the fact that she was acting as my "secretary." She is very Conservative, very Royal Family and all that. I could hear in her voice that my stock jumped fifty-four points.

"What's this," she questioned, "you're hobnobbing with aristocracy?"

"Not with aristocracy, exactly, but certainly with the best of the British Brains Trust."

"You Americans are all alike," Sue said to me on the phone the next day. "You pretend not to be impressed. You simulate an air of egalitarianism, but secretly you're thrilled by it all. You want to hear a joke?"

"Go ahead and tell me a joke."

I got my supply of 10p coins out to stuff in the phone in case the joke ran into overtime.

"Well, there was this little old American couple from the midwest who came to England for the first time. Naturally, they did all the tourist things, and they happened to come upon an official parade in which the Lord Mayor was all dressed up in his grand robes, trappings, and chains of office.

"The Lord Mayor looked around and happened to see on the sidelines his friend Neil – maybe it was Neil Kinnock (at that time Kinnock was the leader of the Labour Opposition) – and he wanted to say a few words to him.

" 'Neil,' he said out loud to attract his attention.

"And the little old American couple kneeled."

"Har, har! Touché, and all that. I get it: a double joke."

Lunch on May 22nd was at Pembroke College. I was invited by Michael Powell, Fellow of Pembroke College and a mathematician. At table I met a number of dons including a biologist whom I shall call Smith. (The presence or absence of the word "the" can serve to distinguish English from Americanese. British: at table. American: at the table.)

"As a biologist you must surely have heard of Victor Rothschild," I asked Smith.

"Heard of him? Certainly. He was my examiner when I came up for my degree."

"Tell me something about him. Anything. My wife and I are having drinks with him later this afternoon. What's he like? What shall we talk about?"

"He's an athlete. Prize cricketer when he was younger."

"That topic won't work for me. I couldn't care less for athletics."

"He's very outspoken. Has his opinions about everything. Formidable man, I should say."

"Is he accessible? Whatever that means?"

"Oh yes. Well, fairly. I'll tell you something else," Smith added, "He's a very brave man."

"How do you mean?"

"During World War II he was in a bomb demolition unit. A new type of German bomb fell and needed defusing. The internal construction of the bomb was unknown. Rothschild volunteered to do the job. But he said, 'I'll go in there with a tape recorder on a very long lead, and I'll speak into it just what I see and what I do. And if I'm successful, well enough and good. And if I'm not, the next man can learn from my mistakes.'"

"Formidable."

"He's won medals for bravery."

MATHEMATICAL ENCOUNTERS OF THE SECOND KIND

7
Sherry at Six

At 5:45 PM, May 22nd we taxied to what, prior to visiting it, I called the *Palais de Rothschild*. I had tried to imagine his house, somewhere off the Cambridge Backs. We would approach the palais via a long *allée* lined with tall cyprus trees, and walk past splashing fountains and formal gardens of teased cunning. Peacocks would be sauntering on the lawns and displaying their thousand eyes with cool hauteur. We would catch sight of – just momentarily – an eleven-point stag in the distant woods.

(Several years later, as if to confirm the possibility of this vision, I read of a remark made by Lionel de Rothschild, a relative: "Every serious garden, no matter how small, should contain a rough wooded area of no less than two acres.")

The medallion above the central portal would display the Rothschild coat-of-arms in blue and white enamel and gold leaf. We would be met by two ushers in mediæval Swiss livery, and conducted to an antechamber. After a decent time had elapsed, the entry of the Baron into his Presence Chamber would be announced by three blasts on silver cornets.

So much for the romantic imagination.

The house turned out to be an elegant modern home, of ample but not elephantine proportions, built along modified Bauhaus lines, and sited among much greenery, quite close to other more prosaic Cambridge residences. There were no blasts on silver cornets to announce The Presence. There might have been a riff or two on the piano because His Lordship was a skillful jazz pianist and an aficionado of this American genre. Some journalists have dubbed Rothschild a "Renaissance Man" and I would not deny him that honor.

The door had been left on the latch. I rang the bell. A white-coated houseman showed us into a small reception hall in which there were glass bookcases displaying many fine editions.

Lord Rothschild made his way in from the adjacent living room. His Lordship was a large, vigorous, stocky man. He was in shirt-sleeves and a baggy woolen pullover, not exactly ravelling, but not right off the shelf either. He greeted us cordially. His voice was loud and deep, and his cultivated accent and tonalities were such that I felt that my own voice was that of a squeaky primitive man from the boondocks. In a few minutes though, I learned that I could thrust and parry quite adequately in my native New England accents. I relaxed and enjoyed Rothschild's beautiful language without feeling apologetic for my own. The English – all of them – are a race of actors and language is important to them in a way that it is not to an American.

After the introductory amenities (are your arrangements in Cambridge comfortable, how did your lecture go, how long will you be staying) he led us into the living room. It was large, though not enormous, and had soft, comfortable furniture arranged into a number of conversational groups. It faced a garden in the rear.

"Do you garden?" I asked.

"Not at all. I rather detest it. We just manage to keep it decent."

Rothschild went to get some drinks. He told us that his wife was out of town – she had wanted to meet us – and that if she had been in Cambridge, we would have been invited to dinner. "Would you like a tomato juice? I believe that Americans are fond of tomato juice when sufficiently laced with vodka."

"I'm not a Vodka-American," I replied, and opted for the more conservative sherry we had agreed to by correspondence.

We talked about mathematics: about prime number theory, about computation (he had just recently bought himself a personal computer and was working away at it), and about what I was doing professionally. We talked about mathematical personalities at Cambridge (he knew them all) and elsewhere. I found that my sense of humor matched Rothschild's and that the afternoon was going along splendidly.

"You are writing another book, I suppose," Rothschild asked me. You seem always to be writing another book."

"Yes. I suppose I am. But you're no slacker at book production. Are you writing another book? What do you say we do a book together? We'll find a topic."

"No. Too old. Too old."

"Have you noticed that when a person is introduced as an author, someone inevitably comes up to him and says 'Oh. You're writing *another* book, I suppose?' "

"Invariably. Now what explains that? You don't go up to your dentist and say 'Oh. You're filling *another* tooth, I suppose? You're doing *another* root canal, I suppose?' "

"And did they go up to Beethoven and say, 'Oh Ludwig, you're writing *another* symphony, I suppose?' "

At this point, I asked him point blank: "I've been wondering why you wrote to me initially? You know, you could merely have walked across the Silver Street Bridge and have gotten all the information you needed?"

"I know. But I've found that the mathematicians here are consummate snobs. If I approached them with my paltry knowledge, they wouldn't have given me the time of day."

"That's true of most mathematicians. Everywhere. But I'd even generalize. I suspect most professors are consummate snobs – professionally, that is."

"I suspect you're right. Let me tell you a story. This happened a half-century ago. I was in my teens and I suppose I haven't recovered from it yet.

"When I was an undergraduate, I wasn't doing so well in maths, and my family thought I'd better go to a crammer before I did my examinations. So they asked about for the most eminent mathematician at Cambridge whom they proposed to hire. They learned that Hardy was the best of the lot."

"G.H. Hardy?" I asked Rothschild. Hardy was one of the Mathematical Greats in the generation from 1910–1940. The idea of Hardy as crammer struck me as though one had called on Einstein to bone up one's son or daughter for the Scholastic Aptitude Test.

"Yes. You knew him, did you?"

"No. I was too young. I studied from all his books though. His reputation was enormous. I've known some of his students."

"Yes. Well, I called on Hardy and told him what I wanted. He asked me a few mathematical questions and I answered him. He thought a while, and then he said, 'Rothschild, you have the mathematical intelligence corresponding to that of a below average schoolboy.'"

"What a thing to say to a kid!"

"An honest man, shall we call him? Then he gave me the name of a man who he said would be most appropriate to cram me."

"Who was that?"

"Hyman Levy. Did you know him?"

"I think so. By reputation, that is. Was he the Levy who in the 1930's wrote a book on Marxist dialectics for Victor Gollancz and the Left Book Club?"

"Oh, you know that book, do you?"

"I struggled through it when I was in high school. It seemed to me the whole philosophic point could have been made in a sentence or two. But I've heard that Levy was an excellent teacher. He wrote a good elementary textbook on something or other – differential equations. He wasn't a research mathematician."

"Yes, he was an excellent teacher. Anyhow I got through to my degree."

"And to rather more."

"Yes, to rather more. But in the 1950's, I gave up my laboratory work. I'd done what I could for biology and went on to other things."

"To banking?"

"I've never cared for banking much. My family wanted me to go into banking, of course. And when I was young I put in a couple years in the City at N. M. Rothschild & Sons, but I never could see it as a lifetime thing. I go in every so often and preside at meetings."

"I suppose there is an affinity between banking and mathematics. You know that the great Felix Klein admitted the elder J.P. Morgan as a Ph.D. candidate in mathematics at Göttingen. That would have been more than a hundred years ago."

At this point, my host turned graciously to Hadassah and suggested that perhaps we had talked enough about mathematics, and that it was time to talk about cabbages and kings.

Hadassah alluded to several small cases of very beautiful butterflies standing on a book shelf.

"Miriam gave them to me. [Miriam Rothschild, famous entomologist and older sister of Victor. Author of, e.g., *Fleas, Flukes and Cuckoos: A Study of Bird Parasites*.] I used to have some nice paintings on the wall. In view of the stiff inheritance taxes, I decided it was time to give them to my children. The law says that if you give them to your children in your lifetime, they can't remain in your physical possession. So I gave them away. The place looked bare and so Miriam came to the rescue."

In this way, and with the omission of one topic on which I'll report separately in just a moment, the hour passed pleasantly. My relationship moved slowly and tentatively, down from the metalevels of Rothschild as abstraction to Rothschild as a man.

Before leaving, I gave Rothschild an inscribed copy of *The Thread*, a lighthearted piece of mathematical fluff I had tossed off several years before, and he, in turn, author to author as it were, gave me a copy of a monograph he had written and printed privately. It concerned the career of his ancestor at the time of Napoleon, Nathan Mayer Rothschild, the founder of the English House of Rothschild.

He sat down at a table, inscribed the monograph to me in that fine script of his, and said,

"This has been very pleasant. Shall we keep in touch? Yes. Let's keep in touch."

When we got to our bed and breakfast I took a look at the monograph and saw that it had been inscribed to me with the initials i.d.a. before my name. I had never seen this abbreviation before. My wife figured it out: i.d.a. = in deep admiration. Very nice, indeed. Who is honored? the Sages asked: He who honors others.

We were on a first-name basis. Well, sort of.

8
Framed Portraits

Before meeting Victor Rothschild I had decided that there were two questions I should like to have answered by talking with him. I have already mentioned the first: why did he write me initially?

He gave me an answer to this question: the snobbery of the mathematical community in Cambridge. I nodded when I heard it, but I didn't believe it was the whole answer.

Here is the second question, formulated out of sheer curiosity and group feeling: was Rothschild a Jew? Now, by this question, I did not mean was Rothschild born of a Jewish mother, or was Rothschild an observant practitioner of the rituals of Judaism, or was he knowledgeable about the beliefs of the religion. Nor did I mean whether he had married into the faith and had brought up his children in that faith.

What I meant was, did Rothschild acknowledge himself as a Jew and was there something in his actions that went beyond the mere acknowledgement?

This was not a question I intended to ask him point-blank. As it turned out, I might very well have asked him. I believe it would not have annoyed him in the least. What I intended to do was to arrive at the answer by inference, by looking and listening. If I had done my homework properly, I could have arrived at the answer merely by reading what he had written or asking around.

In a word, the answer is yes. Lord Rothschild, at least this particular Lord Rothschild, was a Jew.

As Hadassah and I sat in his living room chatting, I noticed that he had four or five framed portraits on display. They did not look like the usual kind of family picture, bride and groom, graduation picture in cap and gown, that sort of thing. I thought they must be politicians. Prime ministers, perhaps. I also thought I recognized one man: Chaim Weizmann, famed World War I chemist, Zionist, and first president of Israel.

"Yes," he said, "that's Weizmann."

"You knew him, I take it."

"Yes. Very well."

"What sort of a man was Weizmann?"

"I could give you my own answer, but I'll give you Winston Churchill's. I was once talking to Churchill and he said to me, 'When that man Weizmann comes into a room, you can't say no to him.'"

"Persuasive."

"Very. A distinct presence."

"A few years ago I spent three months at the Weizmann Institute of Science. Applied Maths. I met Sabin [Albert Sabin, immunologist and developer of the Sabin vaccine for polio, an improved version of the Salk vaccine. A controversial figure. Then president of the Weizmann Institute.] Difficult man, was my impression."

"Yes. Difficult man. And I suppose you knew Pekeris?" [Chaim Pekeris, Head of the Applied Mathematics Department, Weizmann Institute.]

"Yes. He was my 'boss' for those three months."

"Another difficult man."

"Shall I tell you a Pekeris story?"

"Don't. I can match yours any day. I've gone over there occasionally and sat on Boards."

I later found out that in the early days of the State of Israel, Victor Rothschild gave a substantial sum towards the construction of the Knesset (Parliament) building. I might have remembered that the Balfour Declaration, that famous document legitimizing a Jewish State in the eyes of the British Government, was addressed to his uncle, Lionel Walter Rothschild (1868–1937):

November 2, 1917

Dear Lord Rothschild:

I have much pleasure in conveying to you, on behalf of His Majesty's Government, the following declaration of sympathy with Jewish Zionist aspirations. . . .   Balfour

Yes. Lord (Victor) Rothschild is a Jew. An English Jew. Our American tradition asserts that there is no contradiction in juxtaposing these two descriptions. I am not so certain that this is the case in England.

9
The Man Who Has Everything

Who is wise? Whoever learns from everyone. Who is rich? Whoever is happy with what he has. Who is honored? Whoever honors others.

— *Ethics of the Fathers*, IV, 1

So there he was: Rothschild on his own turf. His country house (often described as such) in Cambridge is not a palace, but a comfortable and convenient residence that would not be out of place on the east side of Providence or in Barrington, Rhode Island.

The man himself: vigorous, probing, assertive, demanding, proud, brave, witty, intellectual, knowledgeable, prominent, influential, wealthy, generous. My God, but this man has everything. This man *is* everything!

Just as I struggled with two Rothschilds, the man and the legend, Rothschild himself struggled with this split. He once remarked: "To be a Rothschild is to be accused of being a con-man when you sign your name on a cheque bearing the title of your own bank to pay for a meal in a West End Restaurant" (The *Independent*, 5 Dec. 1986).

How does he stack up against the Wisdom of the Fathers? Does he learn from all men? Yes, I believe he does. Does he honor others and, in so doing, is he himself honored? Yes, I believe this is so within bounds. In my case, certainly; he was very generous in praise of my writing. In talking to him, I felt no real distance. He believes in an Aristocracy of Merit (this is John Adams' term, found in Adams' letters to Thomas Jefferson and much discussed by these men).

Is he happy with what he has? Now there is the sixty-four-thousand dollar question, as we used to say. What is the litmus test for happiness? How can one look into another's heart of hearts and find out what it craves?

In terms of the material things of life, I believe he is quite well satisfied. He is wealthy, but is not one of the greatest of the millionaires. He is easily outstripped by today's Johnny-come-lately billionaires. He lives with money constantly – after all, he is heir to a long banking and business tradition – but he does not live for money.

What does Rothschild want that he does not have? What has he not done that he set out to do, what has he not achieved that he wanted to achieve? What, if anything, wakes him up screaming, at 3:30 A.M., even as you and I wake up, saying to ourselves: how can I get through tomorrow? Let's see how the famous Yiddish writer Sholem Aleichem dealt with the question in one of his stories:

An impoverished Jew from the tiny village of Kasrilevke comes to Paris. Naturally he asks to see Rothschild. (The French Rothschild – around 1890.)

Rothschild is on the verge of throwing him out when the visitor says that although there is hardly anything he can sell him – Rothschild lacks nothing – there is one thing he can sell him.

"What is it?" asks Rothschild.

"The secret of eternal life."

A bargain is struck and Rothschild pays out the price of three hundred roubles.

"Now reveal the secret."

"The secret of eternal life is that you should give up residence in Paris immediately and move to Kasrilevke."

Rothschild is furious. How in the world could that recipe provide eternal life?

"Simple. For hundreds of years now, no wealthy man has ever died in Kasrilevke!"

(I wonder how many interpretations of contemporary medical statistics are based on this kind of logic.)

Malcolm Muggeridge, a popular media personality, talking about Victor Rothschild, said in an interview, "It is ironic. Everyone wants to be rich, but when you meet a very rich man he is never happy."

Rothschild, himself, confirms this: "Having a lot of money does not necessarily mean that one is happy. . . ." (The *Independent*, 5 Dec., 1986).

Does Rothschild's face exude tranquillity? It does not. He smokes rather a lot. He told me he used to be a chain smoker (Balkan Sobranie), and on the doctor's advice decided to give it up.

What, in fact does it mean to say, as we often do, that such and such a person "has everything"? Does it mean only that he has all or many of the things that we ourselves covet? How, in fact, could one conceivably have "everything"? Does one's desire for everything extend to one's children, that they, also, should have "everything"? It mostly does. The desire for the Midas touch goes beyond gold. What would the dangers be as one approached this condition?

To have all would be the end. All tension removed. All desire, all passion spent.

To have all would be to have nothing.

And the other way around, as mystics often assert, to have nothing might very well be to have all.

10
The Plot Thickens; The Heart Quickens

My correspondence with Rothschild continued throughout that fall. His letters now came by regular airmail.

29th October, 1986

Dear Philip,

I was disturbed to get your letter and most recent book because it will, of course, distract me from my ambition to understand complex variables. Distract because I so much enjoyed the other one you gave me that I shall have to get down to this new one at once, which I am, of course, absolutely delighted to do. (I wish you would tell me of a child's guide to complex variables.)

As for the sherry between May 15 and June 15, might we not be a bit more daring and even have a meal together, in London or Cambridge?

With many thanks again.

Yours

Victor

Lord Rothschild

17th November 1986

Dear Philip: [Mostly handwritten]

Thank you for your letter. I will certainly try the book you suggest. The reason is not, of course, a desirable curiosity. It is to understand the substitution of

$$C_k(x) = -2\sqrt{x}\cos(\alpha_k \ln x - \arg p_k) \,/\, |p_k|\ln x$$

for $\mathrm{li}\,x$ in

$$k(x) = \mathrm{li}\,x - (1/2)\,\mathrm{li}(x^{1/2}) - \cdots.$$

[Etc. etc. More on the theory of the distribution of prime numbers. Pretty deep stuff, actually.]

[Some lines on how he was giving up smoking.]
I expect you have read *The Ghost in the Atom* by P.C.W. Davies & J.R. Brown. If not, I will send it to you. It is quite short. But I am sure you know all about Schrödinger's Cat.

Yrs,
Victor

Schrödinger's Cat is an amusing "thought experiment" related to the foundations of quantum physics.

A few days later I was listening to the news on the BBC shortwave. My wife had given me a shortwave set some years before and I listened on a regular basis. This broadcast stated that the British government was blocking the distribution of a book, published in Australia, revealing the inner workings of the M.I.5 (the British military counterintelligence group). In connection with the publication of this book, the accusation had been made (I couldn't catch by whom) that Lord Rothschild was the "Fifth Mole" and was a double agent working in behalf of the Soviet Government.

At this point my relationship with Rothschild took on an added and rather gray dimension. My thoughts about him were turned entirely from the legend to the man, to wondering whether this specific man was guilty as charged, or whether he was the victim of a vicious frame-up attempt. I wondered about the nature of treason and betrayal, and what it means to tell the truth.

Nonetheless, we corresponded as usual, and when we met, my recollection is that there was little change in our relationship.

From the *New York Times*, November 27, 1986:

THATCHER CAUGHT IN 'SECRETS' WEB

London, Nov. 26. Prime Minister Margaret Thatcher is being pressed to explain why her Government is not prosecuting a hereditary member of the House of Lords who was instrumental six years ago in arranging the publication of some of the supposed 'secrets' she is now seeking to suppress.

The development comes as the Prime Minister's effort to halt publication in Australia of a book about the British secret service have landed her in a backwash of emotional controversy here.

The peer in question is the third Baron Rothschild who, before heading a special research unit in the office of Prime Minister Edward Heath, is reported to have served as an official of M.I.5, the counterintelligence branch of the secret service. According to Peter Wright, another former agent and the author of the book that provoked the British suit in Australia, Lord Rothschild arranged in 1980 for the publication in Britain of an earlier book containing many of the same allegations that Mr. Wright has reassembled in his unpublished work called *Spycatcher*.

The earlier book, *Their Trade is Treachery*, by Chapman Pincher, first laid out Mr. Wright's contention that a former M.I.5 director, Sir Roger Hollis, had been a Soviet "mole." In the New South Wales Supreme Court – where Britain's highest ranking civil servant, Sir Robert Armstrong, has been undergoing relentless cross examination for seven days – Mr. Wright's lawyer has contended that the failure of the Thatcher Government to block publication of the Pincher book invalidates its claim that the publication of the Wright book would harm national security.

Sir Robert on the witness stand in Sydney and Mrs. Thatcher in the House of Commons here have both contended that the vital difference between the two cases was that Mr. Pincher was a journalist while Mr. Wright was an official owing what the Prime Minister called 'a lifelong service of confidentiality to the Crown'.

But the distinction between the two cases started to blur on Monday when the *Times* of London reported that Mr. Wright, who had long been presumed to be Mr. Pincher's main source, had received half the royalties for the journalist's book. It blurred even further when Mr. Wright then issued a statement in Australia disclosing it was Lord Rothschild who had suggested that what he had to say about the Hollis affair could best be said in a book.

In Mr. Wright's account, Lord Rothschild's approach "came totally out of the blue." The former agent, who by then was living in Australia, said he was sent a first-class air ticket and invited to come to London for a talk. It was Lord Rothschild, he said, who introduced him to Mr. Pincher and made the arrangements for payment through a Swiss bank account.

"I knew Lord Rothschild to be an intimate confidant of successive heads of British intelligence establishments," his statement said. "I could not conceive of him embarking on such a project without knowing it had the sanction, albeit unofficial, of the authorities. I sensed I was being drawn into an authorized, but deniable operation."

After Mr. Pincher's book appeared in 1981, Mrs. Thatcher assured the House of Commons that the allegations against Sir Roger Hollis – who by then had been dead for seven years – had been thoroughly investigated and found to be baseless. Mr. Wright who apparently concluded that he had been manipulated into an orchestrated disclosure designed to forestall further inquiries concerning the Soviet penetration into the British service, has been striving ever since to reopen the case.

Dale Campbell-Savours, a Labor member of the House of Commons, seized on his statement to file a formal question asking whether Lord Rothschild would be prosecuted. Already last week, in order to demonstrate the consistency of its stand in the Australian court, the Government had to announce that it was investigating disclosures of other secret information by former intelligence officials.

I have trouble with spy stories. The "inner logic" of the operations described confuses me, particularly in the case of author John Le Carré, where against a background of lies, deceptions, and ambiguities the truth is hardly ever perceived clearly. So, when I read this *Times* report, I was confused.

It seemed, on a quick scan, to boil down to this: Guy Burgess, Donald McLean, Kim Philby, Anthony Blunt, Sir Roger Hollis, and now Victor Rothschild? Was this the "Ring of Five" or the "Ring of Six"? And if only five, which was the fifth? Hollis or Rothschild? Could any of this be possible?

On subsequent nights, I kept my ears glued to the BBC short-wave. The story was repeated. Allegations were vented. My local paper in Providence carried none of this. The *New York Times* carried abbreviated versions. The allegations became more insistent.

Our correspondence would certainly stop, I thought; Rothschild is in serious trouble and he'll have no time for it. No letters came from him for a number of weeks. I decided to write. I mentioned – inter alia – the fact that he seemed to be "in the frying pan." He wrote back to me immediately and said – inter alia – that he would soon be out of the frying pan.

Then, a letter from Rothschild to a prominent London newspaper:

Letter to the *Telegraph* (December 4, 1986):

Dear Editor and Readers:

The Director General of the M.I.5 should state publicly that it has unequivocal, repeat unequivocal, evidence that I am not, and never have been a Soviet agent. . . .

Yours truly,
Rothschild

Given that intelligence and counterintelligence agencies are devoted in their very essence to deception, lying, fabrication and dissemination of misinformation, the destruction of privacy, and given they are protected by law from the disclosure of their own secrets, it was hardly to be expected that the Director General of the M.I.5 would respond in any way to Rothschild's demand.

The response that did follow, and on the very next day, was a statement from Margaret Thatcher, the Prime Minister.

> 10 Downing Street
> PRESS NOTICE
> LORD ROTHSCHILD'S LETTER TO THE *DAILY TELEGRAPH*
> OF 4 DECEMBER 1986
> STATEMENT BY THE PRIME MINISTER
>
> I have now considered more fully Lord Rothschild's letter in the *Daily Telegraph* yesterday, in which he referred to innuendoes that he had been a Soviet agent.
>
> I consider it important to maintain the practice of successive governments of not commenting on security matters. But I am willing to make an exception on the matter raised in Lord Rothschild's letter.
>
> I am advised that we have no evidence that he was ever a Soviet agent.
>
> 5 December 1986

This was a rather weak way of putting things, it seemed to me. How would it be to say, for example, that we have no evidence that Dwight David Eisenhower was a Soviet spy? We have no evidence that George Washington sired 27 bastards. We have no evidence that $2 + 2 = 7$. If I were Rothschild, I would have considered Margaret Thatcher's statement unsatisfactory; I would also have to admit that the reply satisfied the demand of his letter. And she did not say: "We seem not to have any evidence," or "we seem not to have any evidence as yet."

What constitutes unequivocal evidence for anything? This may be a question for lawyers. No, not even lawyers, it is a question for metaphysicians. But I got the impression when I heard the announcement that Thatcher was holding back on a complete exoneration.

8th December, 1986

Dear Phil,

Thank you for your letter of November 28th. Of course, I shall not ignore your letter as each of them gives me great pleasure. I think that the fat has stopped sizzling and that the authorities are once again convinced that I am not a Soviet agent.

Enclosed is a photostat of the last paragraph of your letter. I evidently did not make myself clear. Of course, what you say is true but that was not my point.

My point is that in spite of the well-known statement $\pi(x) \leq x$, $\pi(x)$ never does equal x.*

Hence $\pi(x) \leq x$ is never true. Are you still adamant?

Yours

I/v Victor

*given that 1 is defined as not being a prime

On the def. of $\pi(n)$. Example: $n = 10$. There are 4 primes less than or equal to 10, viz., 2, 3, 5, 7. Hence $\pi(10) = 4$. On the other hand, if $n = 11$, there 5 primes less than or equal to 11, viz., 2, 3, 5, 7, 11; hence $\pi(11) = 5$.

The fat was now, perhaps, out of the fire, and our correspondence continued.

16th January 1987

Dear Phil,

Many congratulations on your honour which, if your excursion into epistemology is anything like as good as *The Thread*, does not surprise me.

I wonder if you have read a book by Oliver Sacks called *The Man Who Mistook His Wife For a Hat*. On the off chance that you have not, you might like to read the enclosed which, of course, interested me because of the interest of the twins in Primes.

At the beginning, the writer refers to subconscious algorithms. If the implication is that there is a "conscious" algorithm for the distribution of Primes, he is talking rubbish because as we know, there isn't one, other than the well-known approximations. But is the capacity of the twins in regard to Primes nothing more than an ability for high speed calculation as in the case of other prodigy calculators? That seems to me impossible in the case of the 20-digit Prime. They couldn't have remembered it because where would they have found a reference to that Prime?

What a pity that the writer didn't get a really good Primes specialist to talk to the twins. Would they, for example, have been able to write down the distribution of Prime twins up to 20-digit numbers?

Having recently read *The Ghost of the Atom* and therefore knowing a little about the difficulty to do with "out there" in particle physics, I started wondering whether primes, which I suppose are the fundamental particles of mathematics, are "out there." It seems to me terribly difficult to think straight about primes being embedded in brain cells. But perhaps I am straying into a field near, or at any rate related to, the prestigious prize from the Mathematical Association of America.

Do tell me sometime whether you have any of the feelings of uneasiness that beset me about the twins and their Primes.

Yours
Victor

11
Ruminations on the Philosophy of Betrayal

For weeks, even as I pursued the correspondence with Rothschild, I considered the idea of betrayal. I considered it in the abstract. I considered it in the concrete.

To lie is to betray. Bad people lie. Good people lie. They lie for all kinds of reasons. Our language distinguishes white lies from black lies. "Know the truth and it shall make you free." So says St. John. But is the truth always liberating? Cannot the truth be lethal? Ask a doctor, a psychoanalyst: Am I constantly lying to myself? Would he tell you the truth even if he saw it? Ask a philosopher. The ethics of lying is complicated.

The formal logic of lying is complicated. "A Cretan said, 'All Cretans are liars.'" This is the ancient Paradox of the Liar, famous in the history of formal logic. Was the Cretan lying or telling the truth? This paradox continues to cause heartburn among logicians, and none of the many palliative theories that have been proposed by Tarski, Krikpe and other famous logicians is wholly satisfactory.

It is not easy to know whether a person is lying or telling the truth. Lie detector tests, drugs, sera, torture, various forms of magic, these are some of the ways in which people have sought, over the years, to determine whether other people are speaking the truth.

A person may make progress in his profession by betraying his fellow professionals. Witness: the inside trader.

A person may make progress in his career by falsification and betrayal of the methodology he was taught to adhere to.

I have known a number of men, tough, inflexible men, who have betrayed (often unconsciously) their families for their ideals.

Science progresses by *betraying* ancient principles for new insights.

Wordsworth says somewhere that Nature will not betray those who approach her with an open heart. But to approach nature with a totally open heart means to abandon the mind, to approach nature as raw, unthinking matter. In what way can an elementary particle betray its nature? To be human might even be defined as the possession of the capacity for betrayal.

Are these speculations just playing around with the word 'betrayal' or do they contain something deeper?

The literature of betrayal is vast. The public consumption of this literature is unending. The husband betrays the wife, the wife the husband. Vast and unending, betrayal is one of the primal themes of life.

How does one assess the cost of betrayal?

A man whom you don't know comes to you and says: You have it in your power to save the world. Salvation for mankind is in your hands.

You are pleased with this flattery and by the pivotal position he offers you, but you ask him: what is the price of this salvation?

He answers: Betrayal of your country. God has spoken to me and told me that your country is on a sinful path. It is necessary to get it on track and therefore it's no sin to fulfill God's command.

Think of the famous passage from the Gospels. Jesus said: I say unto you, one of you will betray me, one who is eating with me.

Now answer the reverse question: Whom did Jesus betray?

Or is it blasphemy even to formulate such a question?

His own people, the Jews? Most certainly. More importantly, perhaps, he betrayed his own human nature. That betrayal was allowed and sanctified because, as theology puts it, Jesus has a dual nature: God and Man. This is a statement of psychotheology. Adherence to theology, we know, often betrays us and leads us to slaughter.

God betrays us. Christ on the Cross said so. His physical molecules cried out: *Eli, Eli! Lama sabachtani?* My God, my God! Why have you forsaken me? If God does it, why not Man?

What is an enemy? England was an enemy. France was an enemy. Spain was an enemy. Japan was an enemy. Germany was an enemy. Italy was an enemy. Enemies grow on trees. They are everywhere. Vietnam was an enemy, and now Vietnamese children are studying English in South Providence schools.

The Soviet Union was once a great military ally of the West. I remember how avidly we Americans followed the sieges of Leningrad and of Stalingrad during WWII. I recall vividly how at Langley Field, Virginia, one of the important U.S. Air Force bases, and at one of the prominent bus stops within the base, a map of the Eastern Front was posted daily. Every German and Russian soldier killed seemed to add up in our minds to one less American casualty. Then, when the war was over, the Soviet Union became the Great Enemy.

What is one to think, how is one to act, when it is alleged that a friend, an acquaintance, or at the very least, someone one knows, was a double agent spying for his country's enemy? An allegation is not a proof. But an allegation sticks to a reputation and can damage it severely. One could point a finger and say, truthfully, that this is the man who allegedly was a double agent. The word "allegedly" is the subterfuge that the newspapers hide behind in order to protect themselves from libel suits.

I suppose the answer depends on whether you think the allegations have been cooked up, and what you believe is the ethical status of the particular double agent operation.

In the thirties, when Rothschild was an undergraduate at Cambridge, some of the men who subsequently turned double agent were his college friends. A number of these men were convinced communist ideologues. It is also clear that during WWII and somewhat later, Rothschild played a role in British military intelligence. Perhaps he was involved directly in operations. Perhaps he was a high-level advisor.

Could ideals of communism have led Rothschild to a betrayal? Rothschild claims to be a socialist, in the humanistic sense. Someone said that Rothschild's socialism consists in the deep belief that everybody ought to be as well off as he is.

He claims not to be interested in the theoretical aspects of Marxism. Can a very wealthy man be a socialist? Why not? Isn't this a paradox? No. The whole Russian liberal movement of the nineteenth century, represented by such people as Alexander Herzen, was a movement of the comfortable bourgeoisie and the minor aristocracy. Real peasants in the movement, such as the writer Maxim Gorky, were rare. Sophie Kowalewsky, brilliant mathematician, writer, feminist, socialist and anarchist, was the daughter of a Russian general. She was not one of the starving masses.

Or consider the case of Crown Prince Rudolf of Austria (of the Mayerling tragedy). As a boy, he wrote in his diary: "Uplifting of the soul and progress will be difficult where economic inequality is so marked, that the many poor see in the few rich their enemies. . . . We should ideally consider more or less equal wealth and property a source of moral development. . . ." (Of course, if Rudolph had come to the throne, he would have had to face the realities of what was possible in his position.)

Tolstoy was a Christian Socialist. He might have given up his estates except that his wife talked some sense into him. Prince Kropotkin was a theoretical anarchist. Franklin Delano Roosevelt, one of the most popular presidents the United States ever had, was called a traitor to his class. And so he was, in a sense. The British Empire was destroyed (on paper) by its upper middle-class intellectuals who had profited greatly from the Empire.

Sometime in the fifties or sixties, it became clear that there might have been as many as five or six moles in place in British intelligence. One by one their identities became clear. All these men went to Cambridge, more or less at the same time. They all knew one another. Rothschild let out part of his house in Bentinck Street to Guy Burgess.

The last to be revealed was Anthony Blunt, the art critic, whose character as a mole was known a long time before the public revelation of the fact. Rothschild lent him money to buy art, and rented him rooms in a London building he owned. They were close enough so that Blunt told them that he had willed an important piece of art he had bought for a song (and which had increased mightily in value) to Rothschild's daughter Emma.

I worried: It was easy to establish a case of "guilt by association." There is some indication that an accusation came from a man who himself was a defused Soviet spy turned British agent. There may have been an attempt to frame Rothschild. Why? To deflect guilt from somewhere else? He was vulnerable. There is some suggestion of anti-Semitism.

There is also some indication that Rothschild encouraged and may have subsidized the publication of the memoirs of retired M.I.5 agents in order to clear himself of the charge. These memoirs are easily available in the United States, but not, at the time the affair was made public, in Britain. The matter was then under litigation.

It would seem that Rothschild knows much that he has not made public. He is not required to say what he knows. He has not been put on trial. By the Official Secrets Act, it is probably illegal for him to say what he knows. He may be shielding parties who are innocent but vulnerable.

As his correspondent and as a new friend, I wanted to arrive at my own decision as to his status. Treason strikes me as a particularly odious crime. Stephen Decatur proposed the famous toast: "My country. May she be ever in the right. But my country, right or wrong." How many people today would agree with this? What happens when patriotic duty conflicts with personal philosophy, with family, with friendship? How many would agree with E.M. Forster saying that he would rather betray his country than his friend. Ah, those British intellectuals seem to be different.

Where does one's ultimate loyalty reside? Nowhere. Everywhere. There can be no final loyalty.

Am I betraying the memory of Rothschild's friendship, *a man at whose table I have eaten bread*, even now as I write these lines?

Am I allowed to expose what was a private correspondence because we live in an age when scrutiny has turned into show biz? The stools of former President Reagan have been spread over the front page of the *New York Times* for all to examine.

Rothschild was involved with military intelligence. Even the encyclopedia articles said as much. But was he a traitor to England? I decided he was not.

12

Cryptography

Nonetheless, in the period that followed, vague feelings of doubt washed over me. I came to feel that if England had not been betrayed, I had been betrayed or, at the very least, deceived by Rothschild.

Why, I wanted to know, did Rothschild write to me originally? From the London Sunday *Times*, 30 November 1986:

Rothschild said that the country would benefit from more open government, though, he added gravely, there were many secrets that could never be revealed, thereby teasingly suggesting that he was in possession of many such secrets. *He was concerned about mental decay and said that he kept in intellectual shape with mathematical exercises. Sometimes, he confessed, he felt terribly frustrated with his own mental inadequacies.* [My italics.]

Those few journalists who have interviewed Rothschild have always talked about his humour, his intelligence, the sense of power and experience which he tempered with unexpected modesty.

So there I was, by implication, in the London Sunday *Times*: an instructor to provide mental gymnastics for the man. A kind of Jane Fonda of numbers and equations. Well, sure. I knew this.

But I thought there must be more to it than that. I knew also that mathematics with its up-in-the-clouds, other-worldly "purity," its precision, and its remote abstraction often served people as an escape from the so-called real world. I knew that many mathematical geniuses have a Peter Pan-like innocence: they are perpetual wunderkinder and never grow up. Mathematicians have this character, and I interpreted Rothschild's *Times* remarks as saying that mathematics was helping him escape from some of the concerns that were pressing on him.

But there must be still more, I thought, and I believed (in those moments of my paranoia) I knew what it was.

★   ★   ★

Cryptography is the craft of sending messages to a recipient or confederate in a secret language so that the messages cannot be interpreted by undesirable parties. The craft has a long history that goes back at the very least to Julius Caesar.

Legend has it that when Caesar had a secret message to transmit, he (or his amanuenses) would do as follows: each letter of the alphabet would be replaced by the letter that stood three positions down in the alphabet. Thus 'A' would be replaced by 'D',

'B' by 'E', and so on. When one got to the end of the alphabet, one simply "wrapped around" to the beginning. In this scheme, the message "PUT OUT THE CAT" would be encrypted as "SXW RXW WKH FDW." This type of code is now called in the literature of cryptography the Caesar Cipher.

In the two thousand years since Caesar many types of codes have been employed. One may envision, for example, generalizations of Caesar ciphering in which you go down 4 letters, 5 letters, etc., in the alphabet. Caesar ciphering and its obvious generalizations turn out to be easy to crack.

Code book ciphering is where the cryptographic office issues a book in which arbitrary equivalents are listed; for example,

CODE BOOK

Plaintext	Ciphertext
cat	house
dog	silver
Friday	sweet

etc.

This kind of thing is quite difficult to break, but is subject to various drawbacks such as inflexibility, the physical vulnerability of the code book, etc. Of course, the cipher text in the codebook does not have to make sense; it does not have to be a word in English. For example, "cat" might very well be coded into "eruxp."

With telegraphy, came a kind of ciphering called a "one time pad." This is a form of Caesar ciphering in which each successive letter of plain text is advanced by a different amount to arrive at cipher text. The amount to be added is itself summarized in a second message.

For example, if one lets a = 1, c = 3, e = 5, then the word 'ace' summarizes that the first letter of the plain text be advanced by 1, the second by 3, the third by 5, the fourth by 1, etc.

If the message that represents the shift is itself about as long as the plaintext message to be transmitted, then this type of coding is exceedingly difficult to crack. The long message representing the shifting is called the "pad." In the interests of security, the pad message must be altered frequently, and the distribution of these pads raises certain difficulties.

Cryptography via the one time pad system was entirely automated with the advent of the telegraph. Peter Wright suggests that some of the Military Intelligence Offices combined the "one time pad" with the older idea of the code book.

Code breaking was extremely difficult but feasible up to the age of the computer. One hears of brilliant work done by mathematicians and inspired amateurs in WWII in codebreaking. I can think of Buerling in Sweden and, of course, Alan Turing in England.

With the development of computers that are fast, powerful, small, and inexpensive, cryptography became totally a mathematicians' game, relying on theories of discrete transformations, computer complexity, probability and the ancient but difficult subject of the theory of numbers. In principle, there is hardly a branch of modern mathematics that might not throw up an application to the field of cryptography.

Code breaking becomes impossible within the context of individual human effort, but may again become possible if the breaker has available a computer whose size, speed, etc. is a match for that of the encoder. There is no reason to think that the codebreaker will not have a computer of matching power available, except, possibly, in a situation where the computers themselves are in a rapid state of improvement, and there is an imbalance of computer technology from sender to adversary.

As the craft of cryptography became much more professionally mathematical and totally computerized, a conflict arose between the military information establishment and the mathematical establishment. Developments in mathematics have been totally open since the early 1700's. In the medieval and early modern periods there was some personal competition and rivalry between scientists and discoveries were often hidden or couched in anagrams. That tradition pretty much disappeared by 1700. During WWII certain scientific developments, including some that were strongly mathematical, were deemed confidential or secret and not declassified until after the war.

If I recall correctly, there were four levels of classification: restricted, confidential, secret, and top secret. In my work at the NACA, I was cleared through confidential, and none of the material I myself produced was classified higher than confidential.

In the mid 1970's a number of mathematicians came up with some encoding schemes that were totally new and seemed very promising. The leaders of the National Security Agency wanted to clamp down on the free circulation of information in this area. Some information got out to the mathematical community and is available now in textbooks at the undergraduate college level. A controversy developed between the mathematical community and the security community whose outcome is still moot.

Security and freedom: we require both. Old Roger Merriman, pompous, conservative but popular professor of history when I was an undergraduate, used to wind up his History 1 course by taking his pocket watch out of his vest and swinging it back and forth on its chain like a pendulum.

"The course of history, gentlemen, is that of a pendulum. It is constantly oscillating between the extremes of freedom and those of security. Freedom and security." (Oh, to be called a gentleman once again. Perhaps the pendulum of history will swing back to that.)

One sees the conflict clearly with regard to cryptographic systems, for privacy cuts both ways. We all want it for ourselves, for our personal records and data. We don't want it for the next fellow, especially when he is our military adversary. As mathematicians we should like the freedom of professional expression and information. As private individuals, we want our own privacies protected. Cryptographic encoding of bank messages, etc., is one way to secure that privacy.

The new, highly mathematical systems known as public key systems, developed in the mid 1970's by Rivest, Shamir, and Adleman, were based on the factorization of extremely large numbers into their prime components. By extremely large I mean a number with fifty or more digits. Here is such a number that I have written down at random:

452857689446330909123425436768777123446209000457319786538
56900600700045673865316178674938746200987694613579135246
77111117030253647888122727374607981919243141592314526100
011311566587

Now pose the problem: Factor this long number, just as in school you learned to factor $18 = 2 \times 3 \times 3$. It turns out that this generic question is, at the time of writing, extremely difficult to solve even with the largest, fastest computer currently available. (But it is now less difficult than at the time of conception.)

I cannot go into the details of how such a factorization leads to a cryptographic system that is thought to be extremely secure. But as I have said, the Rivest-Shamir-Adleman system is now part of the textbook literature for college freshmen in mathematics. This system has the feature that you may communicate half of it to your adversaries so that they can send you encoded messages, but by keeping half of the system to yourself, you ensure that they cannot read your own coded messages. Though not beyond my ability to conjecture, I have no private information about the current practices in any of the security or intelligence communities other than what I have read in the open literature. In particular, I have no information about the status of the R-S-A system or its offspring.

Further research along these encoding lines involves the generation of exceedingly large prime numbers, while research along code-breaking lines involves the possibility of the factorization of huge numbers. This is a topic which lately has revitalized some old, deep, highly abstract theorems of algebraic number theory. (It is now thought that the problem of factoring large integers has been cracked, putting into jeopardy the cryptographic scheme. See Coraluppi.)

As the public key system of Shamir, Rivest, and Adleman received the widest publicity in the scientific community, I thought it extremely likely that Lord Rothschild had also read about it. Given his past connections (whatever they were) to British intelligence, and given also his flair for mathematics, I thought that this might turn his mind to prime number theory at the amateur level.

But why his inquiry to me when I was not an expert, and there were so many experts a stone's throw away? The only answer I could come up with again was: precisely because they were a stone's throw away.

13

Innocents Abroad, Once Again

For the month of June, 1987, my wife and I lived in a guest house maintained by Pembroke College. This had been arranged for us by Michael Powell, and turned out to be remarkably comfortable and convenient. A five-minute walk brought us to Market Hill, the colorful open-air market and a twenty-minute walk within range of all the colleges. After an initial period of phonelessness, due to the negligence of the previous resident and the sluggishness of British Telecom, we ultimately got one.

Victor had indicated that he would be in London during the week and in Cambridge on the weekends. I rang him up on Saturday and he invited us for early drinks (11:30 AM) the following day. Lady Rothschild (Tess) would be around and wanted very much to meet us. Victor came to the door in those shirt-sleeves and in that old pullover which, while not exactly unravelling, had not been born yesterday either.

Lady Rothschild, younger than Victor by about five years, struck me as very sensible and very bright, someone whom one would like to get to know better. She hit it off with Hadassah, and the hour passed very agreeably. Their daughter Emma was at home. The conversation, as I remember it, was quite general. People. Books. Ideas. Gossip.

I told Emma that some years ago I had spent a week in Dearborn, Michigan, as a consultant to the Ford Motor Company. While I was poking around in Ford's technical library, I came across a book by an Emma Rothschild raking the American automotive industry over the coals for its numerous sins. "Are you that Emma Rothschild?"

"Yes. I wrote it when I was twenty-three. It scares me now to think I had so much guts then. I'm such a mouse."

"Ha!" I responded, " 'The Mouse that Roared.' You were oracular. Well, if Detroit had listened to you, they wouldn't be in the mess they're in now. Actually, I was surprised to find the book in the company's library."

Emma was at the time she wrote the book an economist, specializing in the economic study of disarmament. She worked and taught at MIT. It turned out that Emma had studied with the MIT economist Robert Solow.

"Bob Solow was one of my students," I told Emma. "Right after WWII, I was a 'section man' in second year calculus at Harvard. Solow was in my class. I was very young. Solow was a couple of years younger."

"How did he do?" Victor asked me, thinking perhaps of his own cramming sessions with the mathematician Hyman Levy.

"Brilliantly. I had to grade all the papers myself. That's what section men are for. Anyway, you didn't have to teach Solow a thing. He'll win a Nobel Prize one day. [Robert Solow won the Nobel Prize in Economics, fall of 1987.] So you see this teacher-pupil relationship makes Emma my 'grand-student.' "

I made a few feints or sallies in the direction of mathematics, but Rothschild was less inclined to discuss the substance of the field and more inclined to talk about its personalities.

I alluded briefly to the fact that he seemed to be out of the "frying pan." He acknowledged that it was so. I didn't really want to pursue this line of conversation unless he seemed eager for it, and I didn't think he was.

A date was set for the next Sunday when we were to come to lunch "with other people I should like you to meet."

14
Glory Be to Intellect in the Highest

An Interview with George Steiner
An Entr'acte

On Monday morning, June 1, 1987, I walked from where we were staying at 12 Fitzwilliam Street to Churchill College. The weather was threatening, a condition that would last through our stay, and I had adopted the English policy of carrying an umbrella at all times. My business that morning was with George Steiner, one of the founding fathers of Churchill College and a brilliant thinker in the areas of language, literature and history.

I was acquainted with Steiner through his occasional reviews in the *New Yorker* magazine and his books. I think, for example, that a *New Yorker* review of his, January 1988, which describes the secularization of the Bible and the loss of the Bible as a common platform for discourse, is a brilliant piece of writing. I had written Steiner in advance, saying that my wife and I would be in Cambridge for a number of weeks and I should like to get his views on a problem.

Steiner came down to the Porter's Lodge to meet me and guide me through the labyrinth of wings and ells that constitute Churchill. He is a short man with a large head. There are times when I am embarrassed by my 6-ft. 2-in. height (no longer so unusual now that infants nearly everywhere are loaded up with massive doses of vitamins), and this was one of those times.

It occurred to me just then that tall/short was one of those basic dichotomies of the world. Rich/poor; East/West; Jews/Gentiles; brilliant/dull; capitalists/communists; beautiful/ugly; and now, tall/short. Has anyone written a history of the world wherein the basic dialectic contradiction is that the short must look up while the tall must look down? I assure you it is important. Napoleon was short. His height played a role in history. According to a well-known saying, if Cleopatra's nose had been a bit shorter, the course of history would have been changed. It is a famous gedanken-nose, to use a term employed by theoretical physicists.

Our conversation – my interview or my audience, as I came to call it later – got off on the wrong foot. By the time I reached Churchill College, the sun was shining. I was embarrassed by my rain gear which was now superfluous, and I alluded to this. Steiner, interpreting this as an attack on the weather in Britain, counter-attacked. How stifling the heat was in the U.S., how bitter the cold, how oppressive the humidity. On the contrary, the weather in England, cool and temperate at all times, was ideal for the life of the mind. Later, he launched into a general attack on the intellectual level in the United States. "The only instance of intellectual excellence in the States was Robert Hutchins and his vision of the University of Chicago."

However, Britain has some culture left, he said apodictically.

"I noticed that Heffer's [a great book store in Cambridge] has put in a large section devoted to VCR tapes."

"There is danger in that," Steiner replied. "In America, the stuff is so terrible that there is no danger any longer. But in England there is a tremendous amount of mediocre material and one is easily seduced into watching it.

"The *Independent* is now the only newspaper in England, possibly in the world, that is worth reading. It's like the *Frankfurter Allgemeine Zeitung* in pre-Hitler days."

My patriotism surfaced, my anger rose. I felt like counter-attacking with, "What are you talking about? Why have the London papers only yesterday written about the new brain drain from the

U.K.? Why do you maintain a government that has all but destroyed the universities, with the possible exception of Oxbridge, and it isn't even clear there. Why are your great libraries and museums in a state of physical decay – just look at them. Why are your philosophy and theology merely branches of grammar? Why are your class divisions still so virulent? Why do I get the feeling, the moment I get outside the Heathrow terminal, that I'm walking into the past? And just what lies at the root of your anti-Americanism? Why do you abhor the country that took you in when you were driven out of Germany? Why do you disparage the country that continues to shower you with honors and engagements, commissions and royalties? The chic of snobbism?"

However, I restrained myself. I hadn't come to hear myself talk or to get into mirror-mirror-on-the-wall polemics. I had come to hear the Master speak. And he spoke. He certainly spoke.

I was interested in the fact that mathematics had grown so much in the last century, both in breadth and depth, that it was rapidly becoming incomprehensible to its own practitioners. Steiner had written a fat volume on the "Tower of Babel" phenomenon (problems arising from the incomprehensibility of natural languages, and the difficulty of translation among them) and I thought it might be useful to draw him out on this question.

"What did you want to discuss with me?" he asked in a manner that was simultaneously pompous and oracular.

I told him. He listened to me hard, in total silence. No back-and-forth as is normal in a conversation. Steiner was the most intense listener I have ever encountered, with ears like an anechoic chamber. His silence forced me to go on and on, far beyond where I would normally have stopped. When he had heard enough, he began to speak. And he spoke and he spoke and he spoke. And I listened to him, rapt, for he is a brilliant man and likes to display his brilliance and enormous erudition. It was hard to break in and I rarely did. I cannot reproduce his lecture here – only the odd crumb of conversation.

I wanted to bring up one point primarily: the increasing babelization of mathematics. I suggested that I was rather glad of this, in a way, because it indicated that mathematics – as a language – shared this feature with the natural languages. The only remedy was, as in natural languages, to install a vast system of translations and expositions: not, say, from mathematical Russian into mathematical English – I am not talking about that – but from one subfield of mathematics into a commonly understood basic mathematical *lingua franca*.

Steiner agreed, and said that the English were brilliant expositors and the "system" in England fostered such expositions. (What system he alluded to was not clear to me; perhaps the system that brings forth such great actors.)

I agreed with Steiner only in part. I answered that I thought English brains were often scatterbrains when it came to exposition. The Russians were better at it. The Hungarians were better at it. This was not to denigrate English creativity in mathematics, but only to question their powers of communicating clearly and to a wide audience just what it was that they had worked out. In any case, the total amount of material thus "translated" was inadequate.

Steiner said that he had spent the better part of his life thinking about communication and had come to the conclusion that lack of communication is also a necessity. One wants private languages that go with private insights and to communicate such insights to small, private groups.

"Such as in much of contemporary poetry?"

"Yes. Blake today would probably have been shoved into an institution, but it took him, in his privacy, to create a tiger that burns. One must create autisms."

I said I knew of a young autistic person, and it seemed to me that the drive of her parents (and of society) was towards normalization and only occasionally towards the expression of her private vision.

"That might be a mistake," Steiner said. "Something might thereby get lost to the rest of us. Something very valuable."

Steiner is a great name-dropper and a great élitist. He thinks that all that matters are the contributions of "the great men." He knows a few great names in mathematics (some of them personally, I suppose) and gives too much weight to the importance of their contributions vis-à-vis the contributions made by the entire mathematical culture. I'm sure he does this in every specialized field he discusses, but it was painfully apparent to me in mathematics.

Accordingly, Steiner's view of the creative world seems to be that it consists of 95% personal genius. The genius is driven by a personal devil or god towards the accomplishment of certain goals for their own sake, toward the fulfillment of a private vision: a drive that borders on madness and which may very well consume the individual genius, and possibly the whole world. A good example, he said, would be the case of Stephen Hawking, the current genius of theoretical physics at Cambridge. Hawking suffers from a terrible disability and is in a wheel chair. He has hardly any body; he is "all brains."

"A story is told about Hawking, that he cried out for the keys to the universe, and God listened to him."

"What chutzpah," I said.

"Hubris," Steiner corrected me.

"The ultimate reality is hidden from us," I continued, paraphrasing the mystics. "Any key simultaneously opens doors and constructs more locks."

I asked Steiner whether Hawking's brilliance was related to his disability. He replied that it undoubtedly was. "One must be very careful not to destroy the private, even if the private is a physical disability. The infant Beethoven would undoubtedly have been destroyed by well-meaning eugenicists. But *you and I are the results of Beethoven.* I would find it impossible to live without Beethoven. And Mozart."

I note here that George Steiner's right hand and arm are defective.

Steiner, who is a chess buff, spoke of having attended the 1972 Bobby Fischer–Boris Spassky match in Reykjavik. He considered Fischer's game to be pure genius. Fischer started out life as a nobody. He had a mixed-up childhood. Someone gave him a chess set and for a while Fischer thought it was a game one played with oneself, taking both sides.

After the match was over Spassky said to Steiner, "Fischer plays as if he and I were one and the same person. He anticipates my moves. There is no distinction between him and me."

Material, I thought, for an Oliver Sacks book: *The Man Who Mistook His Opponent for Himself.* I have met my enemy and it is me.

Our time ran out, and Steiner conducted me back through the labyrinths of Churchill to the street. As I was about to take my leave, Steiner pointed out a private residence up the street from Churchill.

"Do you see the upper window there?" he asked me. "Well, that is the room where Wittgenstein died."

"He always struck me as a very private person."

"Very. In his last days, he was looked after by a woman who is still alive and living in that house. The day before he died, the woman asked him something, such as, 'Would you like a glass of water?' And Wittgenstein answered her, 'Would you please analyze that sentence?' "

I laughed. "He would have been a prime subject for Oliver Sacks. *The Man Who Mistook Semantics for Syntactics and Vice Versa*."

We said goodbye and shook hands.

15
Lunch at the Rothschilds'

When we arrived, two guests were already there and into drinks. Sir Alan Hodgkins, Nobel laureate in biology, and his wife Marian. Victor was in his usual shirt-sleeves and threadbare pullover, Tess in a tweed skirt and blouse.

I knew a bit about Hodgkins' work because in my first years at the National Bureau of Standards my colleagues Henry Antosiewicz and Phil Rabinowitz were working with someone at the National Institutes of Health in Bethesda on the Hodgkins–Huxley equations describing nerve fiber impulses. (Huxley was now Master of Trinity). These were a system of nonlinear ordinary differential equations, to be solved numerically on the SEAC, a "first generation" computer. I remember Henry calling me in to consult on the numerical strategy to be adopted, but I was only marginally involved in the project.

Lady Hodgkins turned out to be American. She had gone to the Dalton School in Manhattan. My wife found that they had friends of friends in common.

The national election in Britain was just a few days off and there was considerable election talk. Among the candidates were Shirley Williams running on the joint Liberal–Social Democratic ticket,

Neal Kinnock for Labour, Margaret Thatcher for the Tories. The incumbent MP for the Cambridge district was Conservative, a university man, and popular with everyone, including the Labourites.

I said that we had seen Shirley riding down Regent Street in a truck, bullhorn in hand. Her party worked enormously hard, and if judged only by hours put in, they deserved to win the Cambridge district.

"Yes, that's Shirley," said Rothschild.

Somehow the subject of AIDS came up, and we tossed it around for a while. I asked Rothschild (as a professional biologist specializing in fertilization) what his reaction to the whole business was, and he said, tongue-in-cheek, that the way to cure it was to forbid the use of condoms. In that way, the plague would run its course amongst, hopefully, an infected minority, leaving the Happy Few intact after a generation.

I told him I thought that this was the most awful social remedy put forward since Dean Jonathan Swift proposed, also tongue-in-cheek, to cure the famine in Ireland by eating up the babies. Rothschild allowed that it was so and then the conversation went elsewhere. Rothschild knows Dean Swift. He had entitled one of his books *Meditations on a Broomstick*, in imitation of Swift's book *A Meditation Upon a Broomstick*, and *Somewhat Beside*.

After drinks we went into the adjoining dining room. Two paintings were on the wall, obviously very valuable though I could not identify the artists. The table was set nicely with china, crystal, and silver bearing an engraved R. This, I thought as I lifted a spoon up and felt its heft, is the silver spoon that was in Victor's mouth when he was born. The service was buffet-style, with kitchen help behind a half-window.

"*Don't* stand on ceremony," Lord Rothschild said to us, "for heaven's sake. Start eating as soon as you've filled your plate. I know Americans wait. We don't here."

"But I can't eat until everyone has sat down. It goes against years of indoctrination."

"Try it. You'll see how easy it is to do."

The conversation turned to the play *Breaking the Code*, then on the boards in London, about Turing, the mathematical genius, the founder of abstract computer science, the code-breaker of whom it was said that he "won WW II for the Allies," the tormented and persecuted homosexual who was sent to prison and who ultimately committed suicide.

"It's an excellent play," Tess said. Victor agreed.

"It's not easy to write a play about a mathematician. You would need some other gimmick," I said. "I suppose that when you come down to it, the homosexuality angle is what makes the whole thing possible as a play. [When *Breaking the Code* played on Broadway, an off-Broadway play on the same topic claimed that Turing was murdered by an intelligence agency.]

"Tom Stoppard wanted to write a play in which one of the characters is a mathematician. Somehow, my publisher got wind of this and wrote to him that if he would like to meet a flesh and blood mathematician, he should meet me. Stoppard agreed to a meeting.

"When I was in London last summer, I called Stoppard up. The time was set, but then he had to take his kid to the dentist. I called again the next day, but he was busy at the theater. So the date fell apart. I read in the papers that he had an opening that had laid an egg and he had to doctor it.

"Actually, I would have been a bad choice for Stoppard to talk to and to model. I'm not sufficiently eccentric. The public wants its mathematicians to be like Professor Moriarty, Sherlock Holmes' great antagonist: utterly brilliant, obscure, remote, amoral, and with more than a whiff of the sulphurous about him. There are plenty such."

I turned the conversation to George Steiner.

"George Steiner. Yes." said Rothschild. "I went to one of his lectures. It was way above me. Couldn't comprehend a word."

16
At Peterhouse

June 9, 1987. Professor Jacques Hayman was head of the Engineering Department at Cambridge. Some years ago, he had spent some months with us in the Department of Applied Mathematics at Brown, and I wanted to convey regards and mend some fences. Hayman invited me to lunch at Peterhouse which is his college. Peterhouse is the oldest college at Cambridge, dating from the 1200's.

After the initial round of "How's so-and-so doing? Very well, considering," Hayman went on to talk about how the engineering students at Cambridge were non-natives to the U.K. They're mostly from the Orient. I told Hayman that the same was true in the States in both engineering and mathematics. Our applications to the graduate program in Applied Mathematics were running $1/3$ American students, $2/3$ others. There was more money, and less brain work, required in other fields. Why sweat when there are easier routes to substantial bank accounts? Such a route was O.K. for first-generation kids in countries where, for the past century, science, technology, and mathematics have led to social advancement, but not in the United States.

Lunchtime approached and we broke up this line of conversation and walked out of the engineering building to Peterhouse. We walked across the lawns behind the great Fitzwilliam Museum, as a shortcut, Hayman opening up private gates with a private key.

The building at Peterhouse in which the Fellows take lunch is very old indeed, with marvelous narrow stone staircases, circular and of small radius, and I imagined that if the BBC-TV wanted to film the murder of the two little Princes, they could find no better set.

The dress at lunch of the younger Fellows in the Cambridge colleges is shirt-sleeves and jeans. The older Fellows wear suits. Hayman is one of the most senior of the senior Fellows.

"Ah," said Hayman to me, "you're in luck. The Master is here for lunch, Lord Dacre. He will be at Head of Table, and I'll place you on his left."

"Lord Dagger?" I queried, faking the sound. I hadn't caught the name.

"Hugh Trevor-Roper, really. Historian."

"Oh, Trevor-Roper. Yes. Of course. Trevor-Roper. I've read some of his stuff."

I jogged my memory and recalled reading Trevor-Roper's book on the last days of Hitler published just after WWII. The British army had been first to get into the bunker, and Trevor-Roper, a young historian, had lucked onto a huge mass of materials. Forty years later, Trevor-Roper made an ass of himself by certifying as authentic a mass of forged letters purporting to be in Hitler's handwriting. This was obviously a topic to stay away from in conversation.

Hayman introduced me to Trevor-Roper. American, Brown University, Applied Mathematics. The Master warmed to none of this. What does one do in such a case? I did not want to eat my lunch discussing the British weather. Well, if he did not care for mathematics, I would talk history with him. Given his track record, I thought I wouldn't have to worry about my ignorance in that area.

I brought up a book I had just read, written by Trevor-Roper's bête-noir (how could I have known this?), A.L. Rouse, of All Souls College, Oxford.

"A deep scholar, Rouse is. Read much. But given to, shall we say, wild flights of imagination? Wild."

Rouse had put together a mishmash of Elizabethiana culminating in a positive identification of the unknown "Dark Lady" of Shakespeare's sonnets. This "identification" was based, partly, on some documents deriving from the Elizabethan physician Simon Forman.

I told Trevor-Roper what I knew about Simon Forman, things that have been already detailed in the chapter on Carpenter and – what shall I say? – he was polite to me. Very polite. It was clear he was not interested in what made Forman's case book so difficult to decode.

Having given me his initial judgment on Rouse, Trevor-Roper went on to more yeasty assessments of his fellow historian and to a lively stream of characterization, unrepeatable here for fear of litigation, which lent so much zest to the dull luncheon meats at Peterhouse that the day was an entirely memorable one.

June 11, 1987. This was a Three Star Day: Election day; Awarding of the Honorary degrees (Hadassah got a ticket) and lunch in the Pembroke Quadrangle for the official participants. These two events were in grave conflict with the third star: my seminar talk in the Department of Applied Mathematics, "Circulant matrices and twisted algebras." A lovely talk if anyone were there to hear it. But I am a pro, and this kind of concern, which worries colloquia chairmen to death, does not trouble me at all. I have spoken to audiences ranging from five hundred to zero, where not even the chairman that arranged the talk showed up.

In the present case, and in view of all the celebrations, my chairman was so thoroughly and happily marinated in wine (like a Danish herring) that after he introduced me and sat down, he fell into a deep sleep and did not wake up until we were well into the question period.

There is a story I like to tell when the chairman at my talk rubs his hands nervously, bites his nails, and says he's afraid not too many people are going to show up. "There's a big basketball game tonight. We're playing Aureola State. There's another lecture down the hall. Walter Cronkite is speaking. Etc. "

The Jascha Heifetz Story. World famous violinist Jascha Heifetz was playing a concert in Helena, Montana. On the morning of the concert, a tremendous blizzard set in over the whole area. At 8:15 PM, when Heifetz and his accompanist looked out at the hall from behind the curtains, they counted only five people in the audience.

So Heifetz came out in front of the curtain and said, "Look, there are so few people here. What do you say we do something like this. We'll all go over to my hotel room across the street and order some sandwiches and some beer. We'll get to know one another; we'll tell a few stories. And that'll be it for tonight."

But one man in the audience raised an objection. "Mr. Heifetz," he said, "I've been looking forward to this concert for months. I live in Galenaville 150 miles from here. I started out driving, but when the blizzard got bad around noon, I abandoned my car in Micaville, rented a snowmobile, and got here. Now the very least you can do for me is to sing a few songs."

About ten years ago, in Salt Lake City, I was scheduled to give a talk. There was a tremendous rain, the basketball team was playing Idaho State, and Walter Cronkite must have been talking down the hall. Very few showed up for me. "Not to worry," I told the colloquium chairman, "I'll put everybody at ease with my Heifetz story."

So I told the story. Afterwards, one man in the audience asked me: "What songs did Jascha Heifetz sing?"

17
Stories and More Stories

June 14, 1987. A very relaxed occasion. Just the four of us: Lord and Lady Rothschild, Hadassah and me.

We had brought the Rothschilds the autobiography of Enid Bagnold, author of *National Velvet* and *The Chalk Garden*, a play that was a smash hit a generation ago. Bagnold's autobiography is one of the most forthright and delightful autobiographies I have ever read. And she wrote it at an advanced age, well into her eighties.

"How did your talk go?" Victor asked me.

"Fine. Considering that it was National Election Day. Considering that the Honorary Degrees were presented. About a dozen people attended. Mike came in rolling from his official lunch in the Pembroke Quadrangle with Prince Philip and a hundred others. Rolling. Mike introduced me quite nicely. Got my name correct. Got the title of the talk correct. Proceeded to sit down in the first row, just below the lectern, and fell completely and hopelessly asleep and slept for one hour exactly."

"I lost an election bet," Victor said. "I bet there would be a hung parliament. Far from it."

He poured out a very dry French wine for us.

"I should be giving up this stuff," Rothschild said, "It's no good for me."

The smallness of the world is particularly well demonstrated when two individuals from remote subworlds find that they know someone in common. Actually, we found many. One such was Meyer Weisgall, the fabulous fundraiser for the Weizmann Institute of Science in Rehovot, Israel. Victor, one of the governors of the Institute, knew him well. I knew Weisgall through the stories of my father-in-law.

Rothschild told us the following story (which we had heard years ago from my father-in-law) and which is alleged to be true. *Si non e vero, e ben trovato.* (If it ain't true, it should have been.) Of course we did not let on that we had heard it; my policy is always listen to the other guy's jokes afresh, whether the other guy is Rothschild or just plain John Doe.

"Weisgall approached a multi-millionaire for a contribution to the Weizmann Institute. After a while, the rich man sent Weisgall a check for $50,000. Weisgall was disappointed with the amount. "A week after receiving the check, Weisgall called up the donor and said that he received the check and would like to invite him to lunch. The donor agreed.

"After polite amenities had been exchanged, Weisgall took the check out of his inner coat pocket and said to the man, 'You know, this won't do. It really won't. This figure does not become a man in your position.' And he took the check between his fingers, tore it up and tossed the pieces into the ash tray.

"The little drama worked, you know. Weisgall got a much larger check."

"Weisgall knew his man," I suggested.

"He knew him like he knew the back of his hand. Weisgall was one of the very great fundraisers. And I've known many."

(Sometime after returning from England, I told this story to my brother, whom I considered to be fairly sophisticated in the world of business. He had been selling petrochemical plants costing millions. My brother was not amused. He thought that Weisgall was a wiseguy. I think the explanation lies in this: my brother, as a businessman, had always dealt with *salaried* people and not with really rich people on their own terms.)

The conversation turned to Teddy Kollek, the then perennial mayor of Jerusalem. "A fantastic man," I said. "It's too bad he couldn't be prevailed on to play a national role and become prime minister."

"Yes, fantastic," Rothschild agreed. "Whenever I'm in Israel, he invites me for lunch to his apartment on Rashba Street. And he always has an Arab friend to lunch with us. He knows that other than himself, I am the most pro-Arab Jew in Creation."

We might have mentioned, but we did not, that Hadassah's uncle, Joseph Bentwich, lived in the apartment below Kollek on Rashba Street. The world is large, but the world is also small.

We brought up the subject of Cambridge mathematical person-alities over the centuries. One of these was James Joseph Sylvester, who matriculated at St. John's and gave his name to a road not far from where we were sitting. He was a very great Victorian math-ematician who wrote, inter alia, a theory of verse and produced a considerable amount of silly stuff as examples of his theory. This reminded me of a couple of clerihews I had read in *Spectrum*, a Cambridge undergraduate mathematics magazine:

> John Edensor Littlewood
> Kept a mistress in Cricklewood
> His "niece" was in fact his daughter
> One rather feels he hadn't oughter.

J.H.C. Whitehead
Had his later life blighted
By the end of his hope
Of being elected Pope.

(Littlewood and Whitehead, of course, were very distinguished Cambridge mathematicians with international reputations.)

We said goodbye to Victor and Tess at the end of June 1987. There was considerable warmth of feeling as we took leave. Tess said to us that she found that at their age it was not easy to make friends. In a few days my wife went back to Providence, and I went on to Austria to attend a conference.

Throughout the fall, I received not a word from Victor. The publication flap still simmered. Peter Wright's book *Spycatcher* appeared in the United States and sold widely. Even though the book was ghosted, I supposed that Wright recouped some of the money which the letter of the civil service law screwed him out of when he retired from Military Intelligence.

Providence Journal, December 22, 1987:

BRITAIN: Book ban lifted. A judge in London yesterday rejected a government bid to permanently ban three newspapers from publishing extracts of *Spycatcher*, a former spy's recollections of misconduct in security services.

"The price to be paid for free speech and a free press in a democratic society will be the loss of some secrecy about the affairs of government and national security," Judge Richard Scott said in support of a challenge to the government ban by three newspapers.

A later report said that this decision would itself be appealed by the government to the Law Lords of the House of Lords.

Providence Journal, January 16, 1988:

BRITAIN: By personal lobbying, Prime Minister Margaret Thatcher warded off an attempt to have the Official Secrets Act liberalized. This act now gives the Government almost complete power to control the flow of information it considers to be related to matters of security.

18
A Gift Suggestion

The year 1988 was probably the height of my correspondence with Rothschild. In that year I received more than a dozen letters, telexes, etc., from him. According to the canons of casual friendship and correspondence, I had perhaps been overdosing on Rothschild. What did I want of the relationship? To be, as Dr. Johnson described his relationship to Lord Chesterfield, his failed "angel," *le vainqueur du vainqueur du monde*? Where could the relationship possibly go? Why press it? Why did it have to "go" anywhere? Why not simply accept it as one of those nice things that occasionally happen, to be enjoyed as it naturally develops?

Conversely, what did Rothschild want of the relationship? Entertainment and a hearty laugh? Apparently I could provide those. Did he want anything more?

February 9, 1988. I called Emma at MIT to ask why I hadn't heard from her father. She said that he had not been well during the fall, but he was better now. I asked whether the newspaper publicity had been hard on him and she said it had. She encouraged me to write him, which I did. I had a luncheon date with her in Cambridge, Mass. set for February 20.

19th February, 1988

Dear Phil,

I have been very remiss in not writing to you, but the second half of last year was not too good for me from several points of view; so I decided to take a long holiday which, as you know, means piles of paper to deal with on one's return. I have now broken the back of the job.

May I ask you two elementary mathematical questions? First, one is always reading chapters in books, or books themselves, about the distribution of primes. But the main subject in these books is $\pi(x)$. I know what this is but if you want to know the distribution of primes, why the distribution of $\pi(x)$ and not of p?

The second question concerns what I call the macroscopic distribution of x, i.e., without the so-called irregularities (which can now be predicted but it takes too long on a computer). If you take the equation

$$\pi(x) = \text{Li}(x) - \tfrac{1}{2}\text{Li}(\sqrt{x}) - \tfrac{1}{3}\text{Li}(\sqrt[3]{x}) - \cdots$$

where $\text{Li}(x) = \int_2^x dt/\log(t)$, is there any reason, apart from the fact that it is forbidden, why one should not devise a polynomial which fits exactly, at least graphically, the above equation? I think I can do it.

I wonder when you are next coming here. I need a little stimulation as my $\pi(x)$ activities during the last two years have been damned by those who know.

I am amusing myself by trying to produce an anthology of micro-essays by a brilliant, aged friend of mine. There are two troubles: first, I don't think he will agree and he still owes me one on Donne. Secondly, I have asked my daughter Victoria to rewrite a piece she did for me on the Music of the Spheres. On the excuse of having to lecture on Old English, she will not produce. Who was that unpopular man, Steiner I think, who said that the Music of the Spheres was Silence? I must reread his book on that subject.

I am also thinking, but only thinking, of forming an Investment Trust which will only invest what the share-buying public is prepared to fork out (assuming they want to) in superconductivity firms or start-up groups.

That is all I am doing except having trouble with my left leg.

Lord Rothschild

February 20, 1988. I had lunch with Emma at the Harvard Faculty Club. We both ordered the tortellini dish. (Why mention this? Only because I feel that food is underemphasized in literature). She will be leaving her position at MIT to become a Fellow at Kings, Cambridge. Kings is the family college on her mother's side. She might possibly be living in John Maynard Keynes' old rooms.

She told me her parents were delighted when she told them that she would be having lunch with me, sent regards, etc.

Victor has had a couple of operations on his leg to relieve some circulatory problem. Apparently things are better now. I told Emma that a while back, I suggested to Victor that we write something jointly. Her eyes lit up. "That would just be great," she said, "but what could it be about?"

"Why, anything at all!"

"How about recollections. Anecdotes?"

"Excellent. I love stories," I said to her.

We dropped the subject. At the time of his troubles, Victor was greatly harassed by the newspapers and the television. Both in Cambridge and in London, they camped on his doorsteps with trucks, equipment, etc. In London, in a rush to get near him, some reporters knocked him down. He is not used to that. Who is? He has never been in the public eye; his work has always been quite behind the scenes.

Emma said the newspapers had been printing out-and-out lies about him. At one point he thought of suing, but then realized he could not win. He would have to appear in court, and the papers would turn the suit itself into a spectacle. He gave up the thought.

"What about Peter Wright's book?" I asked her. "You can go into any bookstore in America and pick it up."

"The same is true in England. Despite the government ban."

There is something spritelike or pixie-ish about Emma. But hard. Determined. No wonder she writes as she does. She outlined her proposed new book to me, in which she questions some of the standard economic measures such as the gross national product.

She is going over to England on March 1, and will bring up the matter of a joint pamphlet with Victor.

February 26, 1988

Dear Victor:

Had lunch with Emma.

She tells me she will be Fellow at Kings for four years. My goodness, back in the original Cambridge! She told me also, if I understood her correctly, that she would be living in J.M. Keynes' rooms. I said to her: great economic footsteps to follow in, and all that, and with the proper ritual, whenever she felt the need for it, she would be able to call up the Ghost of Keynes for advice from time to time.

This reminds me of a story along that line which you may pass on to her.

My most favorite philosopher, and the only philosopher whose books I can really understand, is William James.

William James was interested in parapsychology, and around 1890, set up a laboratory at Harvard to investigate such phenomena. With no pre-assumptions.

Four or five years ago, Hadassah and I found ourselves in an inn near Mount Chocorua, in New Hampshire, where William James once had a summer home.

"The spirit of William James is hovering nearby," I said to her, "and if I approach the matter thoughtfully, I shall be able to call up his spirit from the vasty deep."

"And so can any man," she said, quoting Shakespeare, "but will he come when you do call?"

"Skeptic."

Well, I devised the following ritual to be performed at bedtime. I pronounced quite clearly and distinctly the names of a few of his books and a few of his, concepts. "William James: *Principles of Psychology. The Nature of the Will. Varieties of Religious Experience. Pragmatism. Anti-monism.*"

I followed this with a short peach schnapps, tucked myself into bed, and slept soundly.

In the morning, Hadassah asked me, "Well, did you have any dreams, visitations, para-occurrences, or other unexplainable phenomena?"

"No."

"Did you hear any wails, groans, or any metaphysical principles rattling around?"

"I did not."

"A failure, then?"

"I'm afraid so."

After a fine breakfast at the inn – mein Host fancied himself a gourmet cook and produced a Rolls Royce of breakfasts – I went out for a walk, by myself, through the local farms and cornfields.

I had walked about fifteen minutes, when, all of a sudden, two complete stanzas of what seemed to me to be a rock-and-roll song popped into my mind as a unit. I do not normally listen to rock music. I cannot quote any rock lyrics.

I rushed back to the inn, up to our room, and wrote the stanzas down on the back of an envelope. It was called "Equipment Blues," and dealt with the predicament of a young man who finds he has bought much too much expensive equipment of all kinds.

"William James has spoken to me," I said to Hadassah. "The problem now is one of interpretation."

THE ROTHSCHILD I KNEW

The envelope is hidden away safely in a pile of trash somewhere, and I will dig it out when I think I have located a competent
interpreter.

Regards,

PJD

19
All That Jazz

Ich bin von Kopf bis Fuss
Auf Liebe eingestellt
Dann das ist meine Welt
Und sonst gar nichts

Marlene Dietrich's song in *The Blue Angel*

During our stay in Cambridge in 1987, I had fallen in love with
a cat of my own devising. It came about as follows. Pembroke
College, Cambridge, had a college cat. Her name was Thomas
Gray (female cat, male name). Thomas Gray, the famous poet,
was a fellow of Pembroke and lived for years in a suite now given
over to official cocktail parties. The cat lives in the inner court and
in the staircases, and is fed copiously by one and all including the
cooks. I brought up the cat one day at lunch and one of the Fellows
confirmed what was apparent to me, and went a bit further in
describing the life-style of the cat.

Another of the Fellows, whose specialty was, I believe, the
history of medieval Near-Eastern science, wrote a book in Arabic,
and, for reasons of his own, dedicated the book to Thomas Gray,
the cat. Upon query, he is supposed to have answered, "Why not?

241

I doubt if there are ten people in the whole world who will read my book!"

I put this story in a letter to Marguerite Dorian, a friend who is both an author and an illustrator, and she was charmed by it. By return mail she sent me a letter in which she had drawn caricatures of both Thomas Gray and the eccentric don.

Charmed in my turn, I suggested to her that she do a children's book along those lines. In her turn, she suggested that, on the contrary, I should write the story and she would do the illustrations.

In this way, *Thomas Gray: Philosopher Cat* was born. I imagined a bright young kitten who came in from the fens, took up residence in Pembroke and helped an eccentric don crack an unsolved problem in the history of mathematics.

For all the illustrations, it was not a children's book. It had a moderately successful career and generated rather more publicity than jingle at the till. There was, e.g., a two-page color spread in the London Sunday *Telegraph* in which I was interviewed, and the real cat was "interviewed" through the medium of the Senior Tutor. The book has been translated into German, and just the other day I received a request for permission to dramatize the story for Irish National Radio.

Authors are never, never satisfied – even authors who are tremendously successful. Read, for example, how Edith Wharton was constantly arguing with and prodding her publisher. On a recent trip to London, I found that in Dillon's bookstore, one of the best in the U.K., Thomas Gray was stacked in the section on the Philosophy of Science. For heaven's sake, get her out of there! How many people browse through the Philosophy of Science?

In Blackwell's, the famous Oxford bookstore, I found Thomas Gray stacked among the cat books. A compliment? For heaven's sake, get her out of there! She will be lost. There are more cat books than cookbooks.

8th March 1988

Dear Phil,

Thank you so much for putting me right. I hope you don't mind my periodically using you as a mentor.

As you are philosophizing, it may interest you to know that I wrote to Gerry Piel [Publisher of *Scientific American* magazine] asking him to ask Martin Gardner to write me a letter explaining what he meant by "out there." Gerry Piel said that Martin Gardner never wrote letters and refused degrees. Nevertheless, I got a rather long and interesting letter from him.

"Out there" for Ramanujan [Srinivasta Ramanujan (1887–1920), an Indian mathematician of vast and remarkable intuitive powers] was, as I am sure you know, an Indian Goddess who appeared to him in his dreams. Of course I asked myself, "Are the primes out there and if they are, oughtn't one to be able to describe them?" (Riesel has described them, but I am assured by all my prime specialists that the computer time to apply and work out the distribution using Riemann's Conjecture would be so great as to make the task impossible, though one can do a little and see some dents approximately in the right places.) No twins of course.

One of my contacts, Berry, a very brilliant man, doesn't think the distribution is soluble except in the "rough and ready way" of Riesel; but we know the primes exist "out there"(?). Does it not follow that we ought to be able to describe them and record the result? Macroscopically, of course, there is no problem, but I have to use logarithms when I plot the distribution from 10 to 1016 because I haven't got any graph paper 1010 kilometres long. I have a polynomial which fits the curve exactly, but of course it almost certainly wouldn't if I was not using logarithms.

Your meeting with Emma was a great success.

Don't forget to let me know your exact dates for Cambridge when they are confirmed.

Lord Rothschild

23rd March 1988

Dear Phil,

That old boy, Kronecker, is always reputed to have said "God created the integers. All else was created by man." Surely this cannot be right and he ought to have said that God created the Primes, because all the non-Prime integers can be derived from Primes.

While on the subject of Primes, do you not find it difficult to believe that no number can be a product of more than 25 Primes? Do you by any chance know where the proof of this extraordinary statement is?

Yours
Victor

In reply, I set Victor straight about his "extraordinary statement." Euclid himself would have known better than to make it.

28th March 1988

Dear Phil,

Many thanks for your letter of March 22. We are much looking forward to seeing you both. Why not come and have lunch with us on July 8.

Many thanks for the tutorial.

Yours
Victor
Lord Rothschild

9 April 88

All right. Back to one's Vomit. How can it be true that every odd number > 1 is the sum of at most 27 primes? I'm sure you know.

V

I wanted to bring Victor a present when I came over, so I called up Emma, and she suggested that I bring some jazz tapes. I then arranged with Tom Gleason, who has an extensive collection of tapes, to put out a "menu" of what he had available from which Victor might make a selection.

May 2, 1988

Dear Phil,

Here are some of the things we could tape for your friend:

Jelly Roll Morton, *New Orleans Memories* (and two other LPs less good)

Paul Lingle, *At the Piano* (neo-Jelly Roll)

Fats Waller (some four or five LPs)

James P. Johnson (three LPs)

Albert Ammons, Pete Johnson, Meade "Lux" Lewis (three LPs of boogie-woogie piano)

Willie "the Lion" Smith, four or five LPs; one four-hand w. Mike Lipskin)

Jimmy and Mama Yancey, two LPs (boogie-woogie, plus vocal)

Luckey Roberts, *Ragtime King*

Piano Rags by Scott Joplin (2 volumes), Joshua Rifkin, piano

Eubie Blake, *Blues and Rags*

Primitive Piano (Speckled Red, Billie Pierce. James Robinson, Doug Suggs)

Ralph Sutton, *Piano Moods* (neo-Fats Waller)

Art Tatum (three or four LPs)

Earl Hines (three LPs)

Claude Hopkins, *Crazy Fingers*

Jess Stacy (one LP)

Henry "Thins" Francis (two LPs/neo-Fats Waller)

Kansas City Piano (Count Basie, Pete Johnson, Jay McShann, Mary Lou Williams)

Teddy Wilson, *Statements and Improvisations*, 1934–42

Art Hodes, *Blues*

The King Cole Trio, *The Forgotten Years*

Adam Makowicz, *Adam*

In addition, I have a lot of Count Basie and Duke Ellington piano, although most of it is not solo, but in small band combinations.
I'll be happy to make any of this available to be taped.

Cheers!

PS Also an LP by *Brooks Kerr* (neo-Waller)

Tom Gleason

13th May, 1988

Dear Phil:

It is extremely good of you to think of me. The ones I am
interested in I have marked with a cross. Of course, I don't expect
all of them, but would like the one with Mary Lou Williams to be
included.

We are much looking forward to seeing you July 8th and we
will arrange an anti-jet-lag pick-me-up.

I think I will leave Goldbach [famous unsolved conjecture in
the theory of numbers] et al. until we meet.

[Signed]

Yrs Victor.

Victor's selections were: Luckey Roberts, *Ragtime King*, Claude
Hopkins, *Crazy Fingers*, Kansas City Piano: Count Basie, Pete Johnson, Jay McShann, Mary Lou Williams.

Gleason told me that Victor's selections were very "advanced."
I asked Victor whether he would be willing to tape some of his
own jazz listings for Gleason.

A letter from Victor a week later.

17th May, 1988

Dear Phil,

How much will you bet me you know Gauss's [Karl Friedrich
Gauss, 1777–1855; famous German mathematician] Christian names?

246

How can it possibly be true that every odd $n > 1$ is the sum of at most 27 primes?

Yours

Victor

And shortly afterwards, I read in the *New York Times* that Kim Philby had died in Moscow, 2nd week in May, 1988.

May 23, 1988. A dream in which Victor figured.

London scene. Overall, a sense of frustration. Not being able to get to where I wanted to go. The next logical step is never available. Where is the entrance to the underground? Way up there on the top of the hill.

Met Victor quite by accident at some kind of talk in a hall. As we walked out together, he said, "See you later in the week," when we had a date. I noticed that a hall was close to where the Rothschild Bank was. Sleazy, but in a part of London being gentrified. He parked his car conveniently in his own slot. The hall turned out to be a Labour Hall, whatever that means. Speaker haranguing. Not about labour but about something else, say Womens' Lib. End of Dream.

Friday, July 8, 1988. Lunch with Rothschild. Lady R. and Emma came in briefly later.

He told us a true story about a young genius he'd known, a kid who did A-levels at 9 years old. Rothschild became an "angel" to the kid. He went down to working-class flats to visit him. The kid's mother was there. She said to Rothschild, "Do you know what a bugger is? Shall I tell you? Well, my husband is a bugger." The kid's father ultimately wrote a book with a title something like: *You, Too, Can Raise a Genius.*

Then a Dirac story, of which there are many [Paul A. M. Dirac, 1902–1984, Nobelist in physics]. Dirac was married to the sister of

Eugene Wigner 1902–1995, a famous physicist. The Diracs had a child and Dirac announced it by telling everyone, "Wigner's sister just gave birth."

I responded with, "I'll match that with a Wigner story. In a talk, Wigner referred to the work of a physicist named Zeh, using the German pronounciation Dzeh. Then in his thick Hungarian accent, 'Some people pronounce it Dzeh, some pronounce it Zeh. But in either case, the result is the same.'"

Rothschild told us he had just recently gotten the "golden hand-shake" from N.M. Rothschild & Sons. What on earth could that mean, given that he has "retired" several times now? What on earth does the golden handshake or the golden parachute mean for someone who is very rich? I assume the bank is no longer a family affair and has public aspects.

Rothschild told me that as an aftermath of his leg operation, he ordered a pair of custom-made shoes. "Look at the ones I'm wearing," he said, lifting up his feet. "I've had these shoes for thirty years." Anyway, the shoe man came to his house and measured his feet, and before making the shoes, sent him a bill. "What do you think it came to?" he asked me. I estimated £150.

"£600! Outrageous. But I started the process. I had to go through with it. Good thing I had gotten the golden handshake."

I brought up the case of Anthony Blunt and he replied, "Blunt's a man with a split personality. And both parts get communicated. Likewise for Arnold Hammer."

I brought up the name of Sir Geoffrey Taylor, the great Cambridge applied mathematician. Rothschild responded that when he was doing laboratory work on insemination in insects, he consulted Taylor about the passage of spermatozoa in the carrying fluid. Taylor, he said, could never use the word "sperm." He always transformed it to "cylindrical tubules."

Lady R. has crocheted a cushion that contains major scenes from VR's life, including a panel with cute little spermatazoa.

July 20, 1988. London. I took Victoria Rothschild (Victor's younger daughter) out for a pub lunch. I wanted her to do a plug for the English edition of *Thomas Gray* should one materialize.

This was an appropriate request because Victoria has two cats, Tom & Harry. There had been a Dick, but something happened to him. Victoria has the British equivalent of an American Assistant Professorship in Medieval English at Queen Mary College, London.

Saturday July 23, 1988. Lunch with Rothschild. Present: Lord and Lady R, Hadassah and me. Their cook was not around so Lady R. whipped up some lunch, sending out for some smoked salmon (best I've ever had) and barbecued chicken from Marks & Spencer's food store. Strawberries for dessert.

Lady Rothschild said she might have been an actress. When she was eight, she played a minor role in a play with the great Ellen Terry.

My Story: (Admiral) Lewis Strauss, first chairman of the Atomic Energy Commission, in the presence of generals, admirals, and congressmen whom he had invited to his Virginia farm, put on a yarmulka and said grace.

Victor responded by saying that I.I. Rabi [Nobelist in nuclear physics] thought that Strauss got a raw deal vis-à-vis the Oppenheimer flap [J. Robert Oppenheimer, physicist and A-bomb theoretician accused of disloyalty in the early fifties.] He said that Strauss was in an impossible position.

More conversation: I told a story about a certain William Dodd. I was browsing in the rare book store run by Heffer's and chanced to pick up a book on Near Eastern archaeology written around 1840 by Landseer, father of the artist who did the Trafalgar Square lions. A mysterious marginal note had been pencilled in many years ago:

"This man was the William Dodd who was a preacher and writer and was hung for forgery."

Well now, that hint was enough to set aflame any decent Follower of Obscure Threads. So off to the *Dictionary of National Biography* to check out who William Dodd was. Luckily, Dodd made it in. His life was an object lesson, to which we have listened less and less. He was a popular preacher, who built a temple, lived a fancy life high on the hog, and got overextended. He needed money and needed it fast. He took out a loan and needed the signature of a cosigner. Lord Chesterfield was his friend, and he forged Chesterfield's name on the document. The loan was paid off, but the forgery came to light. In those days (around 1775), forgery was a capital crime.

A "Save Dodd" movement was started. After all, the loan had been repaid. An appeal for clemency was made to King George III. The famous and humane Dr. Samuel Johnson put his name on the appeal. Appeal denied: *pour corriger les autres*. Dodd hung. End of story.

Victor gave me a tape to give to Tom Gleason in return for Gleason's. This was of a BBC radio show, *Castaways*. You are cast away on an island and can take 8 discs with you. What will they be? Parts of the discs are played and intermixed with short bios. Victor was asked to do such a show. His selection was a mixture of classical and jazz, Art Tatum being his god. Selection # 8 was a cantor singing *U b'rosh hashanoh ykosayvoon u v'yom tzom kippur y'kotaymoon, mi yichyeh u mi yomoos, mi v'kitzo u mi lo v'kitzo.* . . . (And on Rosh Hashanah it is written, and on the Fast of Yom Kippur it is sealed: who shall live and who shall die; who at an early age and who not at an early age. . . .)

"This is to remind me," he added on the radio show, "that I am what I am."

He is what he is; and to some extent, the outside world contrives to keep him in that condition. And this means that for better (or often for worse) he must take what the outside world accords to those who are in the public eye. It's hard to have it both ways.

The common feature of Rothschild's selections for *Castaways* is that they are *all bravura pieces*. The technique required to play them is formidable. I think this search for technique, over and above the skillful, extends to the portions of mathematics that he enjoys; this is true even in his speculations about Ramanujan and about the wunderkind described above. He has a great need to deal with the geniuses of this world, defining the term in its spectacular sense.

Later that week I had lunch with Alan Bishop, Department of Education at Cambridge. Bishop views mathematical education as a system of enculturation. He says that all the Asian students are taught mathematics as plug and chug (my term), i.e., as a strictly formal, algorithmic process.

The Cultural Revolution, Bishop said, instigated by Mao Tse Tung, burned all the records of ancient Chinese mathematics. However, there is a repository of such material at Cambridge, so a good deal of it has been preserved.

Cambridgiana: There is a second-hand furniture store not too far from Jesus College whose name is "Auntie Had One And Got Rid Of It." I thought: husband or musical snuff box?

And then there was the large bird that flew accidentally into our Staircase K at Pembroke College and couldn't get out. The bird beat his wings against the windows and flew back and forth for hours. Ultimately, with ladders and brooms and things, and by opening up high windows, the bird was eased out. I spoke to the porter about it, saying that I thought the bird was not very intelligent. The porter, an erect ex-army man with a ramrod back, replied in clipped, precise accents that the bird was definitely not a Pembroke Bird. I suggested that the bird might be a Peterhouse Bird. The porter said no. The bird was definitely a King's Bird.

End of July 1988. From London we flew to Budapest, to attend the ICME (International Congress on Mathematical Education) and give a talk there. Great success. I made numerous new friends there.

18th August, 1988

Dear Phil,

I am prepared to bet you $1 you don't know Gauss's Christian names without, of course, poring over text books.

No galleys yet.

Is there any *English* proof that every odd number greater than 1 is the sum of at most 27 primes? You see, I don't read German.

Apart from Euclid's proof and that of others, is there any tangible evidence of the existence of a prime larger than F_5 (Fermat)?

Victor

Lord Rothschild

I assume you will pass this on to one of your junior number theory specialists.

September 14, 1988.

Dear Victor:

Health & happiness to you and your family for the year 5749. As an added bonus, note that 5749 is a prime number. There are only ten such years in the 5700's. This should stir the imagination of the Kabbalists among us. Greetings to all,

PJD.

27th September 1988

Phil:

You owe me $1 when next we meet because Gauss was christened Johann as well as the two better known Christian names.

Victor

(Note to the executors of VR's estate: this debt as yet unpaid.)

October 5, 1988. After a longish gap – long postal strike in the UK – I sent Victor the manuscript of *Thomas Gray, Philosopher Cat.* Victor thought he might be able to place it with a British publisher.

A telex from Victor dated October 10, 1988: Suggest contact Livia Gollancz, Victor Gollancz Ltd. about Thomas Gray. Also Pevensey Press, Cambridge, Eng. Correct your error about the date of establishment of Pembroke College. Should be 1347.

Telex from PJD to VR: Thanks much for enquiries & errata. Will deliver Gaussian debt in person as I need a good excuse to visit Cambridge in June.

Around October 10, 1988. The *Spycatcher* thing has flared up again in London. The Law Lords have ruled that the papers may reprint and circulate the book. There is an implication in the book that Harold Wilson [Labour Prime Minister, 1964–1970] was a Russian spy!! and that is why M.I.-5 looked into the doings of the Labour Party at that time.

Wright himself later retracted some of his assertions publicly.

When one is once in the spy business and has to lie and sham and dissemble as professional duty, I don't see how one can stop doing it. I can't see what credence the public should put on anything such a person writes.

There was considerable discussion in the London papers as to whether the decision of the Law Lords was or was not a victory for freedom of the press. Some people say it was not, that the decision was simply pragmatic, given that all the information in this case was circulating anyway since the book was published all around the world.

October 24, 1988. a letter from Tess Rothschild enclosing a story from the *Independent* Magazine about some Cambridge cats.

Obviously, she must have enjoyed *Thomas Gray, Philosopher Cat*. I hope so.

28th October, 1988

Dear Phil,

   Thank you ever so much for *Thomas Gray* and for the inscription.

   I do hope my efforts to find a publisher over here will turn out to have been successful.

Yours
Victor
Lord Rothschild

November 3, 1988. I received a note from Victor. He was still trying to place *Thomas Gray* with a UK publisher.

February 9, 1989. Lunch with Professor Trevor Stuart, applied mathematician and Fellow of the Royal Society. He told me that Rothschild once wanted to consult him on a change of variable in a multiple integral. Jacobian and all that. Rothschild brought Stuart, as a gift, a bottle of Mouton Lafitte Rothschild. He explained it this way: "Since you are no longer an undergraduate, I've brought you a better vintage."

A U.K. edition of *Thomas Gray, Philosopher Cat* is in the works. Souvenir Press, London.

14th February 1989

Dear Phil,

   Something is troubling me and I am sure you could put me right in a flash. The first axiom of probability is that for any event E,

$$Pr(E) \geq 0 \qquad (1)$$

The second axiom is that if an event is a certainty

$$Pr(E_1) = 1. \qquad (2)$$

254

It follows from (1) that in certain circumstances

$$Pr(E_2) = O, \tag{3}$$

the O sometimes being written 0.

I thought that if eq. (3) was true, E_2 was impossible; but someone has said to me that that is not true and the event might happen. Given the above axioms how on earth can the event happen?

Yours

Victor

Here is the crux of Victor's letter: in probability theory, if Prob $(x) = 0$, is the event x impossible?

I sent him a long answer as this question relates to the philosophy and metaphysics of probability theory and not to the mathematics as such.

20
Good Morning, Mushrooms! Bonjour, Baked Beans!

As beneficiaries of the good offices of Colin Gilbraith, Bursar, we checked into one of the guest rooms at Pembroke College, Cambridge, June 1989, using it essentially as a bed and breakfast. It was tremendously convenient. The Department of Applied Mathematics and Theoretical Physics was just across the street, as was Fitzbillies' Bake Shop, and the Little Rose Restaurant, offering hearty Greek food at modest prices, was just up Trumpington Street.

Surrounded by food we may have been, but in Cambridge it is quite impossible to find a breakfast "out on the street." Eight-fifteen every morning would find us queueing up with the Pembroke students for breakfast. The contents of the steam tables were absolutely immutable, as though they had not altered since the College was founded in the 1300's: fried eggs, sunny side up, set out four by four, bacon, sausages, baked beans, and a pool of lukewarm tinned tomatoes. Very occasionally, the tinned tomatoes would be replaced by trays of grilled fresh tomatoes.

No mushrooms? But, ah, for the creamy porridge and the Lowestoft kippers that some Britishers dream about! Just for once, please?

Saturday, July 1, 1989. Lunch at the Rothschild's after we had had a brief stay in London.

At the National Portrait Gallery, we had chanced upon a photo of Victor taken in the early 1930's by the famous photographer Man Ray. It shows a handsome young man as yet untouched by the human condition. Rothschild donated it to the National Portrait Gallery. It was hanging near an oil of Sir Isaiah Berlin, an Oxford philosopher, literary critic, historian, and mentor, in some ways, to Victor. When questioned, Victor said that as a photograph by Man Ray it was worth at least £2000.

Upstairs there are portraits of Gladstone and Disraeli by Sir John Millais, and of Arthur Balfour. I had read a profile of Balfour in Piers Brendon's *Eminent Edwardians*. Victor and I talked about him.

Balfour had been at Trinity (Victor's college) and a member of "The Apostles." Recall the cult of fellowship: "I'd sooner betray my country than my friend" — E.M. Forster.

Balfour had a severe case of intellectual, aristocratic, fin-de-siècle lassitude – couldn't make up his mind about anything – as well as cynicism and wit. His portrait shows it clearly. The artist has depicted him as a lily about to expire from lack of water. Balfour's book on philosophy, *A Defence of Philosophic Doubt*, published in 1879 before he went into politics, is an attempt to bolster a flickering faith in religious belief. I was reminded of what Keynes once wrote about Henry Sidgwick, professor of something or other at Cambridge: that he spent his life worrying whether Christianity was true, proved it wasn't, and hoped it was.

Balfour was a Cecil and a wealthy man. He was "put into place" by his uncle, Robert Cecil, Lord Salisbury, then prime minister, who himself had been put into place (politically) by Disraeli. Balfour's advancement is the source of the expression "as fast as you can say 'Bob's your uncle'" as a synonym both for speed and nepotism.

One of the ironies of life is that the most important pro-Jewish document in modern history (the Balfour Declaration) carries the name of this socially anti-Semitic intellectual.

After lunch the phone rang and Tess chattered away for a while. "That was Lady Berlin," she told Victor.

They often played linguistically with the Lord–Lady bit. Indeed, Victor referred to his wife both as Tess and as Lady Rothschild. Both usages might occur in one and the same sentence; which word was used where would make an interesting study in psycholinguistics.

Victor is the only man I have ever met who says he has *never* used a pay phone. He says he has *never* used the London underground. To compensate for these aristocratic shortcomings, he tells stories of how, during the war, he and six GI's sat on a large tree trunk and defecated.

I recall more discussion of virtuosity and bravura performances of all sorts, a favorite topic with Victor.

July 16, 1989

Dear Victor & Tess:

Back home after a quick trip to Denmark, and Hadassah & I want to thank you for your splendid (as always) hospitality. Where, this side of books on theoretical alimentation, does one find samphire [samphire: not the American journalist William Samphire, but any of several Old World plants growing in coastal areas] for lunch? Seaweed it may be, but great seaweed! I always thought samphire was part of the shadow world of elves, like manna or the Rose of Tralee.

It is certainly evidence of the small size of the intellectual world that we should have found an independent connection through Valerie Ayer [She had been Curator of Prints at the Rhode Island School of Design Museum, and was the daughter of Sir Alfred (Freddie) Ayer, who was a famous British philosopher and BBC personality].

She was a rare specimen on the New England scene. Of course, I fell in love with her immediately – as did everyone else – and I couldn't see enough of her – which amounted to two or three times a year. She was married to Brian Hayden who is a professor of clinical psychology here at Brown University. She had previously been married, though briefly.

I never thought of us as being especially close to the Haydens, so when Brian called me after Valerie died, I was very moved. One never knows the role one plays in the imaginative lives of other people.

We went to the memorial service for Valerie held in the University Chapel: music and then readings by Brian. Sang *England's Green & Pleasant Land*: William Blake.

Brian seems to have gotten on quite well with his father-in-law Freddie Ayer, and through Brian I had a bit of a correspondence with Freddie. I wanted to talk to him to see how my ideas about the philosophy of mathematics would bounce off him. I rang him up three or four times in London, but we could never schedule a meeting together.

I wrote to Freddie once asking him what the "dreams of philosophy" were. He wrote back to me immediately. "The dreams of philosophy are to know what is, and to give reasons for supposing it to be the case."

When I read that, I could see that he had abandoned his enfant-terrible, wunderkind, purely logical positivistic stance of his youth. It's not such a bad idea for a lecturer to present a pure, shocking, untenable position, and then to retrench. It clears the air and it makes for good theater. I'm sure Freddie must have been a great teacher.

After Freddie died, I read a number of obits that roasted him for his "youthful" philosophy. Pointless, really.

Returning to Valerie, she really was one in a million. We miss her.

And the strange thing is this: I cannot now bring to my mind what she looked like. Funny.

Best regards,
Phil

Through my friendship with Brian Hayden in Providence, I was made aware of a loose nexus of friendships and hostilities between personalities that might be described as the "New Bloomsbury set." This is one generation after Virginia Woolf, Lytton Strachey, Clive Bell and those folk. They are not Bloomsbury in the literal sense of living in the area. They are less literary and more political. They are more donnish. Among the cast of characters: Stuart Hampshire (professor of philosophy at Oxford); Ronnie, Valerie's mother; A.J. Ayer, Ronnie's first husband; Julian Ayer, Valerie's brother, now a journalist; Isaiah Berlin; Victor and Tess Rothschild.

Valerie knew Emma and Victoria, somewhat. Valerie's maternal grandfather was Sir Thomas Orde Lees, explorer, of the Scott Antarctic rescue expedition fame. Inventor of a parachute, eccentric, wealthy. Val's mother sent Val to the USA in 1939 to get her out of the bombing. Freddie, her father, opposed the move.

Sarah Rothschild, daughter of Victor by his first wife, set up a school for children in Cambridge. Val worked for her around 1962–1964. Sarah believed more in eugenics than in marriage. This led to a rift with her father. The irony was that Victor, whose field was fertilization, might have approved of this. The social reality was otherwise. Today, with artificial insemination, egg implants and surrogate motherhood, Sarah could be seen as in advance of the wave.

23rd October 1989

Dear Phil,

Do you think that, with your great influence and authority, you could get one of your mathematical colleagues to drop me a line explaining how on earth distinct primes come into the Central Limit Theorem?

The attached piece of paper is relevant.

Yours

Victor

Lord Rothschild

As every schoolboy knows, the Central Limit Theorem states

are independent and identically distributed with mean μ and finite

$S_n = X_1 + X_2 + \cdots + X_n$ is asymptotically normal in the sense that:

$$\lim_{n \to \infty} P_r\left(\frac{S_n - n\mu}{\sqrt{n\sigma^2}} \leq z\right) = \Phi(z)$$

A more sophisticated formulation is:

$$\lim_{N \to \infty} P_r\left\{x \in \frac{\nu(n) - \log\log N}{\sqrt{\log\log N}} \leq y\right\} = \frac{1}{\sqrt{2\pi}} \int_x^y e^{-\frac{1}{2}u^2} du, \quad 1 \leq n \leq N \text{ and } n$$

How do distinct primes come into it? (I don't think the question is a Probability and Measure.

October 31, 1989. A brief letter from Victor asking for references on a certain form of the central limit theorem that involves prime numbers.

I am getting the feeling that this is the way Victor has to keep in touch. He cannot become personal on paper, so he resorts to math questions and maintains a warm connection in this way.

28th November 1989

Dear Phil,

Having not heard from you I have tried a little scribbling which is enclosed.

Yours

Victor

[Enclosure]

Let $r(m)$ = the number of prime divisors of m. if p is a prime,

let $\delta_p(m) = \begin{cases} 1 & \text{if } p \text{ divides } m \\ 0 & \text{otherwise} \end{cases}$

Then $\sum_{p \leq m} \delta_p(m) = r(m)$.

Let N be large and P_N the probability law on $\{1, \ldots, N\}$ which assigns equal probability to each integer i, $1 \leq i \leq N$. Then one can think of $\delta_p(m)$ as a random variable and $E\delta_p(m) = 1/p$ and Var $\delta_p = 1/p\,(1 - 1/p)$, δ_p and δ_q are nearly independent if p, q are distinct primes and $p \ll N$, $q \ll N$. Let $X_p = \delta_p - 1/p$ and apply the Central Limit Theorem to X_p:

$$\sum_{p \leq N} X_p = r(m) - \sum_{p \leq N} 1/p \quad \text{and} \quad \text{Var} X_p = \sum_{p \leq N} 1/p(1 - 1/p)$$

Hardy, I think, showed that $\sum_{p \leq N} \sim \log \log N$ as $N \to \infty$. So

$$\frac{\sum_{p \leq N} X_p}{\sum_{p \leq N} \text{Var } X_p} = \frac{r(m) - \log \log N}{(\log \log N)^{1/2}}$$

is approximately normal.

Note I do not believe that δ_p and δ_q are completely independent, hence the need for some approximation. One does not apply the Central Limit Theorem to X_p but to the random variable X_p' which is independent and approximate to X_p.

End of November 1989. I answered the question. It turned out to be the Kac–Erdös Theorem (1939) of probabilistic number theory. Quite deep stuff. I found it in Kac's *Carus Monograph* on independence. These were Kac's "Hedrick Lectures."

I wrote Victor that I was currently thinking about my own Hedrick lectures, and that I was worried that they would turn out to be more flippant than serious. I was comforted by a remark of Harold MacMillan, that it's not a good idea to distinguish too finely between what is serious and what is flippant.

21
Sad News

Victor Rothschild died on Tuesday, March 20, 1990.

The obituary from the *New York Times*, Thursday, March 22, 1990:

London, March 21 (Reuters) –

Lord Rothschild, a scientist and member of the famous banking family who was linked to one of Britains most well-known spy scandals, died Tuesday. He was 79 years old.

His wife, Lady Rothschild, who did not disclose the cause of death or other details, said in a statement issued today, that the funeral would be private and that a memorial service would be held later.

Nathaniel Mayer Victor Rothschild was educated at Harrow and at Trinity College in Cambridge, where he was an outstanding biophysicist.

He succeeded his uncle as the third Baron Rothschild in 1937. He took his seat in the House of Lords, the unelected upper chamber of Parliament as a member of the Labour Party.

At Cambridge, in the 1930's he joined the exclusive debating society known as the Apostles, which included Guy Burgess, Donald MacLean, Kim Philby, and Anthony Blunt, who were later exposed as agents for the Soviet Union.

In 1986, some Members of Parliament called for investigations into whether Lord Rothschild had also been a Soviet spy. Prime Minister Margaret Thatcher dismissed the speculation and Lord Rothschild strongly denied the allegations.

At the start of World War II, Lord Rothschild joined M.I.5, Britain's domestic intelligence agency where he became a senior officer. Later, he recalled, when he realized his Jewish descent would condemn him to a concentration camp if the Nazis took over, he stole a death capsule from his employers.

In 1944, he was awarded the George Medal after defusing explosives hidden in a case of Spanish onions in a ship's hold. In keeping with his style, he carried out the operation with a set of jeweler's screwdrivers given to him by Cartier.

A Jazz Pianist

He was awarded an honorary degree from Tel Aviv University for the "advancement of science, education, and the economy of Israel" in 1971. It was followed in 1975 by an honorary degree from Jerusalem's Hebrew University.

Lord Rothschild was also a sportsman, a jazz pianist and a zoologist.

In 1970, Prime Minister Edward Heath appointed Lord Rothschild to head a review of all British Government departments. Mr. Heath later publicly rebuked Lord Rothschild for his outspoken views on the gloomy state of Britain's economy.

Lord Rothschild spent 20 years [I think 10 years would be more accurate] as an executive with the Shell Oil Company. After just two months working in the family bank, he said he found the job "dull" but remained a director of N.M. Rothschild & Sons and was chairman from 1975–76.

Besides his wife, the former Theresa Mayor, Lord Rothschild is survived by their son James, and their two daughters, Emma and Victoria.

He is also survived by three children from his first marriage, a son, Jacob, and two daughters Sarah and Miranda. His eldest child, Jacob, is the heir to his title.

Even in death it is too much to expect newspapers to give up an opportunity for the insinuation of guilt by association.

From the long obituary in the London *Times*, March 22, 1990, headed "A man of many parts – scientist, government advisor and M.I.5 agent," here is a clip dealing with Rothschild's scientific work:

His own research concerned the fertilization of eggs by spermatozoa whose movements he studied by investigating their heat production and biochemical metabolism. He asked why normally only one spermatozoon enters an egg on fertilization, and in collaboration with Michael (later Lord) Swann, he discovered how an egg 'closed its doors' to other sperm after the fertilizing sperm had attached itself to the egg's surface. His most original work lay in estimating sperm speeds by the mathematical technique called probability-after-effect. . . . He was made a Fellow of the Royal Society in 1953.

From the obituary in the *Guardian Weekly*, April 1, 1990:

He sat as a Labour Peer, but he was 'Hardly One of Us.'

Agreed, he was not a laborer, but who could conceivably have suited as an "us"? A Cambridge don? Not in the perception of Professor Dame Mary Cartwright, famous mathematician, who told me that years ago, in the days when Rothschild was doing laboratory experiments, he was resented because he could pay for help out of his own pocket without asking for university or governmental assistance. I suspect there is no category of "us" that would fit.

Rothschild was Rothschild. He was *sui generis*.

★   ★   ★

FAX: 9 April, 1990. From Miss L. Lindsay, Victor's secretary:

THE LORD ROTHSCHILD GBE GM FRS

A Memorial Service for Lord Rothschild will be held in the West London Synagogue, 34 Upper Berkeley Street, London W1 on Tuesday 15th May 1990 at 6.00 PM. Applications for tickets should be addressed to . . . at. . . .

The ticket of admission read: Please be in place by 5:30 PM. I wondered: for the sake of decorum? Or to allow the easy admittance of a great number of VIP's? We would see.

9:00 P.M., Monday, May 14, 1990. The Royal National Hotel, Berkeley Square, London. I turned on the TV and the BBC 2 was showing a Russian film of the Philby Story. The film was beautifully shot with lovely pictures of Philby's part of Moscow, his apartment, his library, his Russian wife. There were many statements by gruff retired GPU spies, reminiscing about the great old days in harness. In this film, Philby is a national hero of the Soviet Union.

What irony. Why the BBC should want to air this is beyond me. Weeks later, I asked a Kremlinologist about the Philby–GPU connection. He answered that the situation was by no means as clear as depicted. The GPU, he told me, was split into two factions: pro- and anti-Philby.

3:00 P.M., Tuesday, May 15th, 1990. Hadassah was visiting the Tate Gallery with Christine Stuart. I, lolling in bed, turned on the TV to a random channel. This is what I saw:

Question time in the House of Commons. The MP's were giving Margaret Thatcher, the Prime Minister, (who was wearing blue) a hard time. This is par for the course. England is a much more verbal country than the USA. The verbal component is important. Sharp, schoolboy wit.

Mr. Tony Worthington, Labour, Clydebank & Milnegavie: Mr. Speaker, the year 1990 started in January. . . .

Conservative Members: Hooray. Hear hear! (Minor pandemonium.)

Mr. Worthington: This is now May. . . .

Conservative Members: Hooray hooray! Hear hear! (Pandemonium increases.)

The Prime Minister managed a smile.

Speaker: Will the House come to order, etc., etc.

Later in the session. The Prime Minister displayed signs of impatience and weariness.

Margaret Thatcher: I shall answer these matters briefly, for I must soon go to a Memorial service for Lord Rothschild. . . .

And then I thought to myself: Lady, you and I both will be close to one another in the same room.

At 5:00 P.M., Hadassah and I taxied to the West London Synagogue, near Marble Arch. The building, on the smallish side, is built in the Italianate/Moorish style. A number of policemen were posted at the entrance. Tickets were taken and we were shown to our pews. There is, above the Ark, and above the position of the Eternal Light, a cupola-like lattice also constructed in the Moorish style. The synagogue has no central *bema* or reading desk.

Somewhat after 5:30, after most people were seated, the VIP's were shown in. Thatcher was now in black. (Perhaps we are all actors!) The VIP's were followed by the family.

There was a printed program. The service was semi-standard. (After all, this was not a funeral, but a memorial service.) There were three eulogies. A tape of Art Tatum playing the piano. (Charlie Strauss, who is a jazz pianist, told me the piece was way beyond his technical abilities! Lots of hard-driving, strongly rhythmic arpeggios. A Paganini of the piano required for the bravura stuff? No. Liszt? No way. Art Tatum? Gotcha!) Rothschild admired the bravura life and he lived it.

Upon exit, we spoke briefly to Emma and Victoria in the lobby.

Who was there? From the London *Times*, May 16, 1990, I learned who some of our fellow mourners had been. Rothschilds and de Rothschilds by the dozen. Viscounts and Countesses, Barons and Baronesses, Sirs and Ladies by the dozen. Honorables and Dames by the dozen. VC's, OM's and CH's by the dozen. Politicans galore. A passel of professors. A few odd Mr.'s and Mrs.'s.

A few days later I called Lady Rothschild. She thanked us for coming to the service and said she hoped we'd come over for lunch later in our trip. I said we would be spending a few days in Oxford first and wanted to talk with Isaiah Berlin. She indicated he would welcome a visit and gave us his phone number. I called. She was right. We set the time and place.

22

Isaiah's Tales

On Saturday, May 19, 1990 at 6:00 PM, my wife and I met with Sir Isaiah Berlin in his rooms at All Souls' College, Oxford. His study is book-lined and book-bestrewn as befits one of the most brilliant British academics and humanists. It could serve as a model of such to be used in movie sets, stage productions, etc., whenever a scholar's lair is to be depicted.

Berlin offered us sherry but did not take one himself. He was 81 years old and had recently undergone an operation. He got up from the deep chair he sat in by first going down to the floor on his knees.

Our credentials were established easily (my father-in-law Louis Finkelstein; Victor and Tess Rothschild; his and our experiences at Harvard) and although we had never met him before, we settled into a comfortable, chatty relationship. In a certain sense, the hour we spent with him was the high point of that year's stay in England.

Berlin is tremendously learned, witty, and gossipy. He speaks rapidly. He has known everyone of "importance" in the U.K. I recall that many years ago my father-in-law remarked that if he had chosen to go into talmudic studies, he could have set the field on its ears. As our conversation developed, it was clear that he regarded this old option with more than a bit of wistfulness.

In 1948, Berlin told us, he lectured at Harvard, staying in Lowell House. Anthropologist Clyde Kluckhohn, who had been a fellow Oxfordian at Corpus Christi, had been delegated to offer him a permanent position as full professor. Berlin turned it down, saying that he couldn't bear to leave Oxford. Kluckhohn breathed a sigh of deep relief.

"So deep that it was obscene," Berlin related, laughing with considerable gusto.

I replied, "I knew about Kluckhohn because he ran the Russian Research Center, and some of my graduate student friends worked there."

"They got an anthropologist to find out what made the Russians tick," Berlin quipped.

I told Berlin that he had been quite influential in my life through his book *Vico and Herder* and that I and a number of other people were trying to "de-Platonize" the philosophy of mathematics. His *Vico and Herder* had given me considerable intellectual backing with which to push on with the job.

"And very right, too. Do they still believe that mathematics is 'out there'?"

"They do."

"And who are the Platonizers?"

"Well, the School of Analytic Philosophers is by no means dead yet."

I praised Berlin for giving us his interpretation of Vico, saying that the original work is extremely difficult to understand.

"Yes, it is very difficult. But you know, there is a whole group of Vicovians now."

"They are all your children."

He was naturally pleased with my appreciation of his work. He said that he did not work any longer. He said of himself that he had always been a very lazy person. I recalled to myself Tom Gleason's assessment of Berlin: "Absolutely brilliant as a young man. Followed by the typical British academic disease: laziness and inertia after public recognition and adulation."

By this time in our conversation, Berlin had warmed up and was really feeling very comfortable with us. It was clear that he, also, was enjoying the conversation. He has a friendly and genial nature. His eyes sparkle. He is very generous in allowing you your points and your conversational gambits.

I turned the conversation to Victor Rothschild who, after all, was the purpose of our visit. If anything, Berlin became even more open and gossipy.

He had known Rothschild since the mid-thirties when Victor was a Cambridge undergraduate and Berlin was already an academic. He spoke of Rothschild's family and his personality. Lionel Walter Rothschild, the uncle from whom Victor inherited the title of Baron, was a bachelor and a fat, eccentric collector of Things.

Walter once rode down the street in a carriage pulled by four ze-bras. Miriam Rothschild wrote a biography of her uncle Walter.

Around 1916, when Victor was around six years old, Victor's father Nathaniel Charles Rothschild committed suicide. This fact was carefully concealed from the children. Victor first heard about it from a schoolmate, and Berlin paraphrased the revelation this way: "Well, I may be only so and so, but at least my father didn't kill himself."

Devastated, Victor asked his sister Miriam. She also knew noth-ing. (Naturally there is nothing about this in the *Who's Who* type of book or in the *Dictionary of National Biography*. It is interesting to think that every age has the things it needs to conceal. Will suicides ever come out of the closet?)

I asked Berlin whether the 'cause' of the suicide was known.

"Well, it is thought that he was unbalanced."

"No scandal, that sort of thing, to trigger it?"

"Not at all."

"Did Victor's mother remarry? She was a young woman, after all."

"She did not. I knew her. They called her Roszika. She was Hun-garian; came from Budapest. The daughter of wealthy Hungarian Jews by the name of von Wertheimstein. Quite a nice woman, actually. Her family was wiped out in the Holocaust."

Berlin said that while Victor was brilliant, he (Victor) knew full well that he was not among the most distinguished of scientists. He used to play the game of asking his visitors, "Who is first in the field? Who is second? Name the top ten!"

I told Berlin that this was a game, I was sorry to have to report, that my fellow mathematicians liked to play. G.H. Hardy was a master of this game, comparing various mathematicians to famous cricketers. I added that I absolutely refused to play this game.

"And very right, too."

"Speaking of world famous mathematicians, I assume you knew Hardy?

"Oh, yes. Quite well."

"What was he like?"

"Well, here's a Hardy story for you. Hardy was a fervent atheist. He kept a score card in which he ticked off his victories as against God's victories. If, say, he learned that a priest had been killed in an accident, that would be one point for him!"

"Victor," he continued, "made his mistakes. The recommendation of the Rothschild Commission that the U.K confine its investment in scientific research to the bottom line of profitability was devastating. It turned the government support of research exclusively to problems of immediate concern."

"It is still hurting the country."

"Indeed, it is."

"On the other hand," Sir Isaiah went on, "his recommendation on the Concorde supersonic plane turned out reasonably well." (The recommendation was that the Concorde should not have been pushed. But having come so far with it, the project had better be completed.)

I moved on to the accusation that Rothschild was the "fourth" or "fifth" man in a spy ring for the Soviets.

"It was very sad," I said, "that Victor's last days were darkened by the accusation of being a traitor to his country."

Berlin took up this conversational gambit with vigor.

"A very sad thing. It devastated Victor completely. The last few years have been hell for him."

"Then this would have been during most of the time I knew him. I could not have guessed from his manner. What was the real story?"

"The truth of the matter is very simple. Victor owned a flat in London which he had let out to Blunt. He knew Blunt from undergraduate days in Cambridge. This flat became what might be called a male homosexual brothel. When this was revealed, Victor's name was mentioned over and over again. This was picked up by the writers of spy shockers and other types of scurrilous material and insinuations were made. The increasing number of insinuations and near allegations of treason distressed him very much.

"He was a man with an extremely high sense of personal integrity and of family integrity. He was a man with a very high sense of patriotic duty. Everyone could see that.

"And then Victor, in desperation to clear his name absolutely and irrevocably, did something that proved to be unfortunate.

From his M.I.5 connections, he was quite friendly and on good terms with a certain Peter Wright. Now Wright had a complaint against the M.I.5 service relating to retirement funds, and he wanted to air that and many other complaints. Victor paid Wright (who was in Australia) to do a book, on the assumption that Wright's book would, among other things, exonerate him completely. Now Wright was not a writer, so Victor involved another man by the name of Pincher to assist in the preparation of the manuscript.

"When Wright's book was published it ran afoul of the Official Secrets Act. It was banned here, although it was easily available in Australia, the USA, and even here in England. Her Majesty's Government tried to pressure the Australians to ban it, but this impugned Australian independence and integrity, and they wouldn't go along with it.

"At any rate, although easily available, Wright's book officially was under a ban, and when it became known that Victor had subsidized the production of the book, a charge against him was proposed on the grounds of aiding and abetting a criminal act. The police investigators were sent to his house and he was questioned for hours and hours. It was a nerve-wracking process for Victor.

"The unfortunate publicity that surrounded the matter was increased because Wright and Pincher squabbled publicly about their respective split of the royalties. The book sold many copies.

"Victor tried to get his friends to speak up for him in Parliament. Heath [Edward Heath, ex-Prime Minister] was a very good friend of his, but Heath would not speak up."

"Why not?"

"That edge of doubt, I suppose. Victor never forgave Heath for this betrayal."

"But Heath came to Victor's memorial service."

"Yes, he did."

"And so did Thatcher. Was there any suggestion of anti-Semitism in the affair?"

"I should say there was not. But to get on with the story. In desperation, Victor did a damn fool thing. He wrote a letter to the newspapers demanding that the Government clear him unequivocally. For days Thatcher did not respond."

"Was this because the Official Secrets Act forbade her to discuss publicly any aspect of an M.I.5 matter?"

"No. I don't think so. But of course, such an interpretation of the law would have been a considerable convenience to her. Ultimately, she came forward and said weakly that the Government had not a shred of evidence against Victor."

"When I read that, I thought the statement was as weaselly as you could get. But Thatcher was at the Memorial Service and so was Heath. I suppose that their presence was a symbolic act and constituted a complete vindication. And then there was that third eulogy by that young politician Waldegrave [William Waldegrave, M.P.] that explicitly denied any wrongdoing by Victor. And Waldegrave is a Tory."

"Yes. Waldegrave is the son of a Marquess. Victor 'picked him up' as a bright young lad for one of his think tanks. I must say, Victor was a bit of a snob, you know."

"I know."

"Brains were important to Victor. Very. But the son of a Marquess with brains, well, that was an even better combination."

"Waldegrave spent at least five minutes of his eulogy in clearing Victor. For me, that was one of the surprises of the service. I wasn't sure whether the affair would even be mentioned. Actually, the service was full of surprises for me."

"What were they?" Berlin asked.

"Many. First of all, playing the Art Tatum record. Hardly ecclesiastical music. Hardly requiem music. Then the allusion to the spy affair. Then the inclusion in the service of the passage 'Let us now praise famous men.' Hardly standard. A bit on the side of vanity, don't you think?"

"From *Ecclesiasticus*. Apocryphal material. You know there were a couple of sentences in the Christian version of *Ecclesiasticus* that the family wanted to be included. But they are not in the Hebrew version, and so the Rabbi would not allow it."

"Might one say that the whole unfortunate affair derived from the sin of pride?"

"One might, but that would be an expression of self-righteousness."

"And then, I was quite generally surprised by the fact that the service included all the things that would have normally been said in a Jewish funeral service. Including the song *'El Molay Rachamim'* (God, full of compassion)."

Berlin's phone rang and interrupted our conversation.

"I have an appointment with a Russian lady. But look, let's spend ten more minutes together."

"I hope you can find out what makes Russian ladies tick. And speaking of ticking, when my correspondence with Rothschild began, I wondered whether he was a Jew – I mean in the sense of a positive identification with the Community of Jews."

"Oh yes, very much so. You know, Victor's first wife was converted. An odd thing that, but there you have it."

"And are his children Jews? I mean in the same sense."

"I should think they are."

This was followed by some remarks about Victor's relation to his children. Berlin said that Victor had hoped that the Rothschild name would always be above suspicion. We did not see any reason to push the matter further.

We all got up to leave. Hadassah and I followed Sir Isaiah down the staircase to the Porter's Lodge where a number of men, dressed formally for dinner, greeted him.

Berlin took his leave of us, saying to my wife, "Please give my best wishes to your father. And may he live to one hundred and twenty. Do you know why one says one hundred and twenty?"

She replied "I think because Moses lived to one hundred and twenty."

"And Moses was forbidden to enter the Promised Land. Do you know why that was?"

"Tell us."

"There are two explanations. There is an official explanation and there is an unofficial explanation. The official one is in the Bible. Moses struck the rock to get water, thus displaying a lack of faith. The unofficial one comes from the Midrash. When Moses went to Midian to see Jethro, his future father-in-law, Jethro asked him who he was. Instead of identifying himself as a Hebrew, Moses answered 'I am from Egypt.' This deliberate ambiguity cost him his entry."

My wife responded, "I take it that kind of ambiguity will not cost Victor his entry."

"No, it will not. Goodbye. Goodbye."

23
A Symbol

Months passed during which I was working up a draft of my Hedrick Lectures, later published as *Spirals: From Theodorus to Chaos*. Early in September, 1990, I sent a letter to Tess, asking her for permission to dedicate my book to Victor.

9th September, 1990

Dear Phil:

Victor would have been very pleased at your suggestion of your dedicating your lectures to his memory. Yes, his correspondence with you helped him *enormously* during those horrible *Spycatcher* years.

Victoria and Emma join me in sending you both our warmest affection and say how pleased they are at your idea.

Tess

I also wrote to Isaiah Berlin, telling him of my proposed dedication, and also saying that I had enjoyed his article in the *New York Review of Books* on Joseph de Maistre.

9 October, 1990

Dear Mr. Davis:

It is very good of you to have written to me as you have. I am glad you are dedicating the book to Victor's memory – his value to the world, quite apart from his great celebrity, is not sufficiently appreciated yet.

Thank you very much for your kind words.

Yours sincerely,

Sir Isaiah Berlin

Lunch with Brian Hayden on November 6, 1990. He has much gossip that came to him through his late wife and father-in-law. He told me that Isaiah Berlin's wife is a Rothschild (on the French side). He was her third husband, she his first wife. Married late, no children. Very wealthy. Homes in NY, Riviera, etc. Her first husband was a French count who died young.

In June 1991 I was back in London and had an appointment with Isaiah Berlin in his pied à terre in the Albany in Piccadilly. The Albany is just across the street from Fortnum & Mason's and is adjacent to the Royal Academy of Art. It seems to have been built in the early 1800's. There are plaques on the wall commemorating the famous personalities who lived there.

Berlin thoroughly approved of my plan to write a memoir of my experience with Victor. He conjectured that Tess would be very agreeable to the project.

I said that at first Rothschild had been a abstract symbol for me, and that over the four years of our friendship the symbol had incarnated into an individual.

"What was he a symbol of?"

"Well, of Rothschild, but of no specific Rothschild. Infinite wealth. Infinite power and influence. Great philanthropy. Palestine. The Balfour Declaration. Wine in France. Wine in the Carmel. The tomb at Ramat ha Nadiv. In short, Rothschild: the "Head" of the Jews. And Rothschild was an abstract concept, like the Presidency, not lodged in any one individual."

As I recited the items of this litany, Berlin smiled, nodded his head, rubbed his hands together, and said "Yes, exactly. Splendid. Bravo. Go on. Tell me more."

And then, when I had finished, he said, "But the realities of this particular Rothschild were different. He wasn't very wealthy (by Rothschild standards, that is). He had been screwed out of a great deal of wealth by two of his cousins who, when he was a young man, offered him what turned out to be Class B shares in the Bank. And since he was then interested in science and academics, he accepted them."

I confessed to a dilemma: I would like to work up a memoir, but of course, the accusation of spying occurred during the middle of our correspondence. How should I treat what I knew of it? Simply ignore it?

"No, you mustn't ignore it. Plough right into it. As you knew it. The man is as clean as a whistle. No doubt of that. He simply knew these people. And when the political pornographers started up with their innuendos about his connection with Blunt, etc., Victor went a bit berserk. He did some damn fool things that he should not have done. He got Wright to come from Tasmania to do a book. Wright was very upset by his having been screwed out of a proper retirement from the M.I.5. Victor was in the M.I.5 – military counterintelligence against the Nazis – during WWII. Victor thought that Wright's book would set the record straight. It didn't, of course."

Sir Isaiah said that Tess had been a bit of a radical when she was young. "And then, after the war, John Strachey [(1901–1963), Marxist, author of *The Coming Struggle for Power*, a book that had quite an international vogue in the 1930's] tried to interest Victor in Marxism. Strachey presented Marxism as a scientific doctrine. It was often touted as such. Victor, as a scientist, was interested in it only as an instance of what might be said to be scientific."

We also spoke about Berlin's latest collection of essays. He said that the one on Joseph de Maistre had been written years ago, submitted to a journal on the history of ideas, and rejected.

"That's a good story for the young to hear," I said. "One should not allow initial discouragement to play too large a role."

"Well, I put it away. Didn't look at it for years. But recently a young friend dug it out. Worked on it. Straightened it out. And then it appeared in the *New York Review of Books*."

He said that the joke embedded in my proposed title, *My Rothschild Story*, would not be understood in the U.S. or in the U.K. Of course, he understood it. Berlin proposed something like *The Rothschild I Knew*.

We got on to a discussion of relativism and pluralism, which was the subject matter of one of his recently reprinted essays.

"I like vanilla. You like strawberry. Recognize these facts. Nothing at all is said as to which is better. This is relativism.

"I like vanilla. You like strawberry. I think vanilla is better. I can't prove it is better, but I'm willing to argue the case. This is pluralism. Neither relativism nor pluralism implies tolerance of your views. "

I expressed my fondness for William James who was a pluralist. Bravos from Isaiah. I spoke of my "social constructivist" views of mathematics. More bravos.

He seemed to be in agreement with my view that by and large Europeans like to create systems, while Americans don't. I expressed my suspicion of systems. He nodded. [Remark after visiting Norway. I can now understand an old joke that I had read – I think it comes from the English mathematician Augustus de Morgan – to the effect that Europeans sit in their cafes and devise systems. The systems consist of two parts beer, one part tobacco smoke, and very little reality.]

Our conversation was winding down. By way of a coda, Berlin told me the following story in Yiddish. He said it had been told to him by Rabbi Israel Goldstein. Once, in a Russian or Polish village there was a wealthy skinflint. There was also a "professional" *schnorrer* (beggar, panhandler). The *schnorrer* set his sights on breaking down the skinflint. A matter of professional pride, you know. So he went to him with a heartrending story. He said that in this very village there was a certain widow with six children and that he was begging on her behalf. The widow was disabled, the children were starving. Their clothes were rags, they lived in a hovel.

The heart of the skinflint was softened and he gave the *schnorrer* some money for the widow.

Some months later, the skinflint met the *schnorrer* on the street.

"How is the widow making out?"

"She is doing fine."

"She still lives in this village?"

"Oh yes."

"Do I know her? Who is she?"

"Know her? Of course I know her. She's my wife."

"Your wife? But you told me she was a widow!"

"What skin is it off your nose that I'm alive?" (*"Vos artet Aych dass Ich leb?"*)

24
Random Variables

The title of this section is a standard piece of terminology in the theory of probability. It is also the title of a book by Victor

Rothschild that deals not with probability theory, but with family biography.

If, as a schoolboy, I had been able to solve a certain problem in geometry, I might not have become a professional mathematician. If, as a college freshman, I had not struggled in English composition, I might not have written as much as I have and would not have made an explanatory mistake. If, in pursuing my profession, I had not left St. Andrews, Scotland in advance of my plans, I would not have made a good friend of a Cambridge resident and not have visited Cambridge annually. If I had not been a regular visitor to Cambridge, I would not have my own Rothschild story to tell.

Random variables? If history is not a record of "ifs," how is it then that the word plays such an important role in our thinking? What makes the combination "if, then" the basic syllogism of formal logic, of deductive mathematics?

Push the thought just a bit further and ask how the matter appears from the other side? What were the "ifs" and the "if nots" that led Rothschild to write to me? And what were the consequences?

Sir Thomas Browne wrote in *Urn Burial*: "What song the Syrens sang, or what name Achilles assumed when he hid himself among women, though puzzling questions, are not beyond all conjecture."

25
Mathematics as Literature: Prime Number Theory

I shall attempt to explain (neither deductively nor completely intuitively) the final mathematical topic taken up in my correspondence with Victor Rothschild. This was the so-called Erdös–Kac Theorem of probabilistic prime number theory. I shall also add some speculations on the accessibility of higher mathematics to interested non-professionals.

I have always assumed that by just looking at a recipe a practiced cook will be able to tell pretty much what the dish will taste like. I am not so sure about a corresponding statement for musicians. If one hands a musician a score – even the conductor of an orchestra – will the musician be able to tell pretty much what the piece will sound like when played? And when it comes to professional mathematicians, I know it just isn't so.

Give me a piece of mathematics and the chances are good that I might not be able to make any sense out of it at all. I may not even be able to identify it as a piece of legitimate mathematics, as opposed to a piece of complete gibberish. There are so many specialized fields of mathematics, each with its own notions, vocabularies, methods, goals, and criteria (stated and unstated), each part of a separate culture if you will, and I am versed in only one or two of them. Give me a piece of mathematics at random, and it might take me weeks of hard study to interpret it and months of hard study to convince myself that what is asserted is, in fact, the case. And I do not think myself exceptional in this regard.

Mathematics is touted as a "universal language," frozen in time: the mathematics produced in Germany will be comprehensible in Korea, for example. And so it is, in some ways. It is also the case, as I have hinted, that I may not be able to understand what my mathematical colleague across the hall has produced and may have grave difficulty in getting into the minds of my mathematical predecessors of centuries ago, as I have no opportunity to ask them to explain.

To some extent, one's ability to comprehend instantly will depend on how the material is written up. If it is written up in the classic style of Euclid, as a bare and brief sequence of axioms, definitions, theorems, and proofs, heavy on symbols and with light or non-existent explanatory matter in English or any other natural language, then this kind of material will be very difficult indeed to comprehend. This kind of writing is what editors of mathematical journals (with some exceptions) prefer. It costs less, it follows a great tradition, and it is the hallmark of mathematical "maturity." What needs to be fleshed out can very well be left to the reader to do as a spare time exercise. It may be a minimalist presentation, but "in principle" it is all there.

On the other hand, mathematics can be written in an expository style, in an almost literary style, with the elements just mentioned reversed in emphasis. If this is the case, and if the basic material falls within the basic training and experience of the reader, then such a book may be read with enjoyment almost in the way that a novel can be read.

My candidate for a field that allows instant and wide mathematical comprehensibility is the theory of prime numbers. I have kept up with this field largely as literature; I have never "done anything professional" in it other than to take several graduate courses. The fact that this field is essentially about simple arithmetic makes its statements easy to understand. These statements are often enormously difficult to establish with rigor, and this provides them with a special challenge and panache. The prime numbers are loaded with peculiarities and this gives the field zest and flavor. The field is full of unproven conjectures that are easily comprehended by both by amateurs and professionals, and this provides challenges and fascinations for both groups.

Though dealing essentially with elementary arithmetic, that is, with the integers 1, 2, 3, 4, ... and the four arithmetic operations $+$, $-$, $\times$, and $/$, number theory, in its deeper aspects, makes use of analytic methods. These are methods that involve advanced calculus, including the calculus of complex imaginary numbers. This material is normally a part of the education of all professionals. Abstract algebra, including group and field theory as well as algebraic geometry, also put in substantial appearances, but I would rule myself out as one with a "reading or conversational knowledge" of such matters.

I have listed in the references to this chapter several recent books on prime number theory that I have been able to read and enjoy as literature.

★   ★   ★

The integers 1, 2, 3, 4, ... have for thousands of years been the source of application, wonder, inspiration, and mystery. Resident among them as a distinguished subset are the so-called prime numbers: 2, 3, 5, 7, 11, ... While perhaps of lesser application in the affairs of science and technology, primes have been the source of much more wonder, inspiration, and mystery.

A prime number is one that cannot be split into the product of two other integers,s other than the obvious split into 1 and itself. Six can be split: $6 = 2 \times 3$, while 7 cannot. Thirty-six can be split in many ways: $36 = 2 \times 18 = 3 \times 12 = 4 \times 9 = 6 \times 6$. Thirty-seven cannot be split. Put the matter in the following slightly absurd way: a rectangular egg box intended to hold precisely three dozen eggs can be designed in five different ways. A rectangular egg box intended to hold precisely 37 eggs can be designed in only one way: as one long row.

The integers 1, 2, 3, 4, ... can therefore be separated into two classes, those that are prime and those that are not prime. The integers that are not prime can be split and are called *composite numbers*. The integers 0 and 1 play a special role in prime number theory (would you regard $0 = 0 \times 6 = 0 \times 31 = 0\times$ any number as splits?); they are not considered primes.

From the point of view of multiplication, the prime numbers are the building blocks or the atoms out of which all the integers can be constructed. The meaning of this is that all integers can be factored down to a set of prime components. Thus:

composite: $36 = 2 \times 2 \times 3 \times 3$. Two different prime factors.

composite: $444 = 2 \times 2 \times 3 \times 37$. Three different prime factors.

prime: $37 = 37$. One prime factor.

If one disregards the order of the factors, there is only one way in which the splitting can occur. This statement is known as the *fundamental theorem of arithmetic*. While familiarity with multiplication soon convinces one of the truth of this statement, the surprising thing is that it is possible to devise peculiar and specialized arithmetical systems for which the fundamental theorem is false.

It has been known since antiquity that *the number of primes is unlimited*, or, as one says, is *infinite*. Given a prime number, one can always find a larger one. Thus, as opposed to addition, wherein all the integers can be created by the successive addition of the single integer 1, when it comes to multiplication, an unlimited number of prime building blocks are required to do the job.

Here are the primes below 100:

2 3 5 7 11 13 17 19 23 29 31 37 41 43 47 53 59 61 67 71 73 79 83 89 and 97.

There are 25 of them.

Here are the next hundred years or so that are prime:

1997 1999 2003 2011 2017 2027 2029 2039 2053 2063 2069 2081 2083 2087 2089 and 2099.

There are 14 of them in the 21st century. It would seem that the primes are thinning out a bit: in the first century of the following millennium (3000–3100), there are only 12 primes.

If you believe that special events will occur in years whose numbers are special, then you should mark down the years just listed and wait and see how special they turn out to be.

All prime numbers save the number 2 are odd, for even numbers can be split in half. One of the things that struck mathematicians very early on is that the primes seem to occur erratically. The gaps between successive primes (always even numbers) can be as low as 2; e.g., 3, 5, 7; 11, 13; 17, 19. The gaps can also be arbitrarily large. There is a string of 653 consecutive composite numbers just after the prime

$$11, 000, 001, 446, 613, 353.$$

It turns out that it is very hard to get a grip on just where primes occur.

To determine whether a number is or isn't prime, one might proceed naively as follows. See if the number divides evenly by 2. If it does, stop: it's composite. If it doesn't, go on and see if it divides evenly by 5. (You don't have to see whether it divides by 4, for if it did, it would have already been divisible by 2 and stand categorized as composite.) If it divides evenly by 5, stop: it's composite. If it doesn't, go on and see if it divides by 7.

Continue this process, trying to divide successively by the primes, until one divides by the largest prime that is less than or equal to the square root of the number being tested.

Example: if the number to be tested is 21, you need not test for divisibility by 7, for this would have already been made clear by the test for 3: $21 = 3 \times 7 = 7 \times 3$. Generally, if one divisor is less than the square root of the number in question, the second divisor must be greater than the square root.

This procedure can be systematized, and then becomes a process known as the *Sieve of Eratosthenes*, developed in the (3rd century BCE. Though this procedure goes back several thousand years, sieve methods of increased subtlety are profitably employed today in prime number testing and theory.

Despite the erratic nature of their occurrence, much is known about prime numbers. Too much, in fact. Paradoxically, *it is true quite generally in mathematics that the more that is known about a particular subject, the more that remains unknown.* Therefore, there are hundreds of books, filled with thousands upon thousands of theorems worked on by thousands of individual mathematicians over the millennia, while hundreds upon hundreds of interesting conjectures about the prime numbers remain unproved.

Generally speaking, the field can be divided into the following main areas of concern:

* Tests for primality. Numbers that have hundreds if not thousands of digits.

* Special computer programs and techniques in the field. These range from how to do the arithmetic of gigantic numbers expeditiously to efficient computer programs that implement theoretical criteria.

* Factorization of numbers of gigantic size, say, a thousand or more digits.

* Distribution of the primes in the large and in the small throughout the integers. This distribution is often described in terms of the function $\pi(n)$, defined as the number of primes in the interval from 2 to n.

* Special formulas for generating prime numbers.

* Prime numbers of special, preassigned form.

* Primes and probability theory.

* Applications of prime numbers that are of interest outside mathematics itself.

These areas can be pursued both theoretically and experimentally. (Years ago they were pursued via pencil and paper computations; today, using digital computers). The questions that can be raised within these areas are often expressible in simple arithmetic terms, and for that reason they can explored and enlarged upon by amateurs. At the same time, these very questions may be so difficult to answer that they baffle professional mathematicians who have at their disposal methods and techniques of the most profound difficulty and subtlety and who have devoted their lives to them. From a very simple question in arithmetic, one is plunged immediately into some of the deepest mathematics that has ever been contrived.

Prime number investigations, therefore, are wide open to amateurs, professionals, computer buffs (specialized commercial software is available), people who love to deal with large numbers, people (often termed neo-Pythagoreans) who see in individual numbers mystic connections with the universe, people who get their jollies by breaking records and getting their names in a "Guinness Book of Mathematical Records." The largest known prime is now such-and-such. I will find a larger one!

Note: As of the writing of this book, the largest known prime is the Mersenne number $M(859433)$, where $M(n) = (2^n) - 1$. It is a number of 258716 digits. But this fact may very well be out of date at the time of printing.

Last but hardly least, the field is open to people who have a commercial interest in the applications (e.g., cryptography – important not only for military and diplomatic operations but also for data security in our computerized age). What may strike the outside world as idle curiosity about numbers may appear to the insider as the very breath of life itself.

The distribution of the prime numbers within the integers exhibits two contradictory features simultaneously. On the one hand, it is erratic, chaotic; on the other hand, it exhibits features of regularity. In a certain sense, any theorem relating to the prime numbers is a statement about a certain kind of regularity; the fact that insight into the distribution of the primes can be gained by methods of probability is an indication of their random nature. The famous Prime Number Theorem tames their haphazard nature by asserting that as the integer n becomes larger and larger, $p(n)$, the n-th prime number, gets closer and closer, in the sense of ratios, to $n \log(n)$. (log = natural log = log to the base e = 2.71828....)

Each of the specialized areas within prime number theory mentioned above can be and has been made the subject of at least one book.

The Erdös–Kac Theorem (1939) relates to the distribution of the number of factors of integers n, and is a fine example of the way mathematics can extract order out of chaos. Though the final statement of the Erdös–Kac Theorem is deterministic in nature, its underlying spirit comes from probability theory, in particular the formulas for the normal distribution of the sums of large numbers of independent events. How so?

In mathematical probability theory, two events A and B are defined as independent if the probability of A and B occurring simultaneously is the product of the individual probabilities, i.e.,

$$\text{prob}(A \& B) = \text{prob}(A) \times \text{prob}(B).$$

If we think now of all the multiples of three, then, in a loose sense, we might say that one third of the integers are multiples of three. Similarly, one fifth of the integers are multiples of five. Since integers that are both multiples of 3 and 5 are multiples of 15 (and vice versa) and these constitute 1/15-th of the integers, then switching informally to probability notation, we can write

$$\text{prob(mult 3 \& mult 5)} = 1/15 = (1/3) \times (1/5)$$
$$= \text{prob(mult 3)} \times \text{prob(mult 5)}.$$

Thus, the event of an integer being a multiple of 3 and the event of it being a multiple of 5 are independent. The numbers 3 and 5 are not special. The same observation works for any two (or more) mutually prime numbers.

Note: this will not work if the numbers have a common factor. One fourth of the integers are multiples of four; one sixth are multiples of 6, but a multiple both of four and six is a multiple of 12 and vice versa. However, $(1/4)(1/6)$ does not equal $1/12$.

If now for integers n and primes p one defines the function

$$s_{p(n)} = \begin{cases} 1 & \text{if } p \text{ divides } n \\ 0 & \text{if } p \text{ does not divide } n, \end{cases}$$

then $s_{2(n)}$, $s_{3(n)}$, ... are statistically independent functions whose sum is $w(n)$, the number of distinct prime factors of n. This leads us to conjecture that the distribution of the values of $w(n)$ will be described approximately by the normal law of probability (the famous bell-shaped curve that has been getting in the newspapers so often in connection with social statistics).

To be precise, one has the Erdös–Kac Theorem:

Designate by $N(x, a, b)$ the number of integers in the interval $[3, x]$ for which the inequalities

$$a \le \left(w(n) - \log\log(n)\right)/\sqrt{\log\log(n)} \le b$$

hold. Then

$$\lim_{x \to \infty} \left(N(x, a, b) \right)/x = \text{normal prob integral from } a \text{ to } b.$$

To put it coarsely, this says that the values that $w(x)$ takes on for x between 3 and n are very close to being distributed normally, with mean $\log\log(n)$ and standard deviation $\sqrt{\log\log(n)}$.

I mentioned that, given the right type of exposition, mathematics may be "read as literature." Let me show how, in the case of PNT (prime number theory), elements analogous to literary ones appear.

A novel gives a description of the behavior of certain individuals within a group of individuals. PNT gives a description of the behavior of the prime numbers within all the integers. There are many subplots, many individual threads that can be followed up.

Even as humans often exhibit contradictory natures, mathematical objects often paradoxically exhibit contrary natures. Thus, in PNT, the distribution of the primes, $\pi(n)$, is both erratic and regular.

The action of a novel moves in time; the development of PNT (or of any mathematical subject) also moves in time insofar as more and more becomes known or becomes more precise as time goes on.

Example: In 1845 Bertrand conjectured that there is at least one prime between every integer greater than 1 and its double. This was established rigorously by Tschebyscheff in 1854. Bertrand's conjecture can be expressed in terms of the π function as

$$\pi(2n) - \pi(n) \geq 1, \quad \text{for } n \geq 2.$$

Much more precisely, it was found later that if $n > 4$,

$$1 < (1/3)(n/\log(n)) < \pi(2n) - \pi(n) < (7/5)(n/\log(n)).$$

If one selects $n = 100$, for example, these inequalities say that the number of primes between 100 and 200 is between 7 and 31. (In point of fact, it is 21.)

Ramanujan gave a proof of the lower bound in 1919.

Often, but not always, a novel moves its characters to a conclusion. Such-and-such happened to them at the end, and that's all the author is ever going to tell you about them. By contrast, mathematics is open-ended, moving in time through many authors. Particular questions may be answered, but no topic is ever completed. Though further prolongation of a topic may exhaust the interest of the reader, it does not exhaust the logical possibilities.

Example: For many years, the statement that $p(n)$ is asymptotic to $n \log(n)$ was unproved and the object of intense efforts. It was regarded as the basic theorem of PNT. Finally, in 1896, two mathematicians, Jacques Hadamard and Charles de la Vallée Poussin, working independently, proved it and rather more. They established that

$$\pi(x) = \mathrm{li}(x) + E$$

where $\pi(x)$ is the number of primes $\leq x$, where $\mathrm{li}(x)$ is the "logarithmic integral", or the integral with respect to t of $1/\log(t)$ from 2 to x, and where E is an error term whose size is of the order

$$E = O\big(x \exp(-A\sqrt{\log(x)})\big).$$

Instead of putting the question of the distribution of the primes to rest once and for all, this accomplishment merely heated up the activity. So, in the century that followed, alternate and simpler proofs were sought and found, as were sharper estimates for E.

Insofar as the fundamental prime number theorem expresses the behavior of the primes in the long run, simple inequalities were sought which are valid for all values of x (with the possible exception of a finite number at the low end).

Here are two inequalities, dating from the early 1960's:

$$(x/\log(x))\big(1 + 1/(2\log(x))\big) < \pi(x), \qquad x \geq 59$$
$$\pi(x) < \big(x/\log(x)\big)\big(1 + 3/(2\log(x))\big), \qquad x \geq 1.$$

These inequalities were discovered by Barkley Rosser and Lowell Schoenfeld. They appeal to me particularly because I had graduate courses in analytic number theory with Schoenfeld.

A novel must have tension in order to maintain the readers' interest. PNT (and all mathematical disciplines) exhibits the tension of not knowing the truth or the falsity of informed conjectures, and of the uncertainty in balancing the reasons in favor of the conjecture against the reasons opposed. Thus, in PNT it was not known as late as 1995, and may still be unknown, whether there are an infinite number of primes within the integers of the form $(n^2) + 1$. On the one hand, the arithmetic sequences $an + b$ where a and b are relatively prime integers (e.g., 4, 7, 10, 13, 16, ...) are known to contain an infinity of primes (Dirichlet, 1837). On the other hand, among all integers, those of the form $an + b$ have density $(1/a) > 0$, whereas those of the quadratic sequence $(n^2) + 1$ have zero density. This rarity might make all the difference as regards the latter sequence.

As we approach the year 2000, it is not known if there are an infinity of twin primes, or pairs of primes whose difference is two: 5,7; 11,13; .... Although for this and many more such statements there is abundant experimental or heuristic evidence, rigid proofs have not yet been forthcoming.

When and if the question is resolved one way or another, the tension will be dissipated, only to be transferred later to other unproved conjectures.

Human persistence and endurance, human striving, the desire to outdo, are exhibited amply in PNT; one need only consider the title of Ribenboim's *The Book of Prime Number Records*.

Style and aesthetic values, often hard to pin down in literature, (though attempts have been made to mathematize them!), find parallels in mathematical exposition. The style of Euclid, admired and imitated by many, may be poison to others. Aesthetic values of literature and graphic art, which often have been sought in a balance between the simple, the ordered and the complex, have parallels in mathematics. Keats' equation of the true and the beautiful is as equally valid and invalid in mathematics as in art.

I hope that this section has provided a demonstration of how mathematics can be read as "literature." Expositions of mathematics done in a literary manner will contain substantial discussions of relevant history, heuristics and philosophy. Computer graphics provides the possibility of striking and often suggestive visual understanding. With effort, the subject can be changed from a widely incomprehensible, dry-as-dust concatenation of abstract symbols into the stories of human adventure. My correspondence with Rothschild was one such adventure.

Acknowledgments

Chapter I

Professor Bernhard Neumann, Australian National University, Canberra, reawakened my interest in the history of "Napoleon's Theorem" and provided me with much information.

Chapter II

I should like to thank the following people for much that was helpful: Joseph Davis, David Park, David Pingree, Ihor Sevčenko, Charles Strauss.

Chapter III

Christa Binder and Clifford Truesdell provided me with some unusual background material.

Bibliography

Chapter I

For a proof of Napoleon's Theorem that is within the scope of high school geometry, see, e.g., Coxeter and Greitzer, referenced below.

Allen, Robert Loring. *Irving Fisher*, Blackwell, Cambridge, 1993.

Baker, H.F. A remark on polygons, *J. London Math. Soc.* (1942), 162–164.

Berkhan, G. and Meyer, W.F. Neuere Dreiecksgeometrie, *Encyclopedie der Mathematischen Wissenschaften*, III AB 10, Band III, Heft 7, pp. 1173–1276. B.G. Teubner, Leipzig, 1920.

Boyer, Carl B. *A History of Mathematics*. John Wiley & Sons, New York, 1968.

Cavallaro, Vincenzo G. Sur les segments toricelliens, *Mathesis* 52 (1938), 290–293.

Carnot, L. *Oeuvres Mathématique du Citoyen Carnot*, Basel, J. Decker, 1797.

Chang, G. A proof of a theorem of Douglas and Neumann by circulant matrices, *Houston Math. J.*, 7 (1981). No. 4.

Coxeter, H.S.M. *Introduction to Geometry*, John Wiley & Sons, New York, 1961.

Coxeter, H.S.M. and Greitzer, S.L. *Geometry Revisited*, Random House, New Mathematical Library, 1967, 63–65.

Davis, P.J. Cyclic transformation of polygons and the generalized inverse, *Canadian J. Math.* 29 (1977), 756–770.

Davis, P.J. Cyclic transformations of *n*-gons and related quadratic forms. *Linear Algebra and its Applications,* 25 (1979), 57–75.

Davis, P.J. *Circulant Matrices,* John Wiley & Sons, New York (1979).

Douglas, J. Geometry of polygons in the complex plane, *J. Math. Phys.* 19 (1940), 93–130.

Douglas, J. On linear polygon transformation, *Bull. Amer. Math. Soc.* 46 (1940), 551–560.

Faifofer, Aureliano. *Elementi di Geometria,* 17th ed., Venezia, 1911.

Finsler, P. and Hadwiger, H. "Einige Relationen in Dreieck" *Commentarii Mathematici Helvetici,* Vol. 10 (1938), 316–326.

Fischer, Joachim. "Napoleon und die Naturwissenschaften," Franz Steiner Verlag, Wiesbaden, 1988.

Fischer, W. "Ein geometrischer Satz," *Arch. Math. Phys.* 40 (1863), 460–462.

Fisher, Irving Norton. *My Father Irving Fisher,* Comet Press Books, New York, 1956.

Forder, H.G. *The Calculus of Extension,* Cambridge University Press, 1941.

Kline, Morris. *Mathematical Thought from Ancient to Modern Times,* Oxford University Press, 1972, 304–317.

Laisant, C.-A. Sur quelques propriétés des polygones, Assoc. française pour l'avancement des sciences, *Compte rendu* 1877, 142–154.

Laisant, C.-A. Théorie et applications des équipollences, Gauthier-Villars, Paris, 1887.

DeLaunay, Louis. *Monge,* Editions Pierre Roger, Paris, 1933, 222.

Mackey, J.S. Isogonic centres of a triangle, *Proc. Edin. Math. Soc.,* 15, 1897, 100–118.

Maritain, Jacques. *The Dream of Descartes,* Philosophical Library, New York, 1944.

Medawar, P.B. *Advice to a Young Scientist,* Harper & Row, 1979.

Neumann, B.H. Some remarks on polygons, *London Math. Soc. J.*, 16 (1941), 230–245.

Neumann, B.H. A remark on polygons, *London Math. Soc. J.* 17 (1942), 162–164.

Neumann, B.H. Plane polygons revisited, *Essays in Statistical Science, Papers in Honour of P.A.P. Moran*. J. Ghani and E.J. Hannon, eds., *Journal of Applied Probability*, Special Vol. 15A, 1982, pp.113–122.

Neumann, R. Geometrische Untersuchung eines Ausgleichstransformators für unsymmetrische Drehstromsysteme, *Elektrotechnik und Machinenbau* 39 (1911), 747–751.

Neumann, Richard. *Symmetrical Component Analysis*, Pitman, London, 1939.

Osserman, Robert. *The Poetry of the Universe*, Anchor, New York, 1995.

Pedoe, Daniel. Thinking geometrically, *A.M. Monthly*, 77 (1970), 711–721.

Pedoe, Daniel. *A Course of Geometry for Colleges and Universities*, Cambridge University Press.

Phillips, Andrew Wheeler. 1844–1915, privately printed, New Haven, 1915.

Phillips, A.W. and Fischer, I. *Elements of Geometry*, Harper, New York, 1896. Last printing, 1943.

Rutherford, W. "VII Quest. (1439)," *Ladies' Diary*, No. 122, (1825), 47.

Scriba, Christoph J. "Wie Kommt 'Napoleons Satz' zu Seinem Namen?," *Hist. Math.* 8, 1980, pp. 458–459.

Vrooman, J.R. *René Descartes*, Putnams, New York, 1970.

Wetzel, John E. Converses of Napoleon's theorem, *Am. Math. Monthly*, Vol. 99, 1992, pp. 339–351.

Wetzel, John E. E-mail correspondence, November 30, 1995.

Yaglom, I.M. *Geometric Transformations*, Random House, 1962 38–40.

Chapter II

For the Lamia:

Philostratus, *Life of Apollonius*, translated by C.P. Jones. Penguin Classics, 1970.

The number of books and articles on Napoleon and his age is enormous. Eckart Klessmann estimated the total number to be in excess of 400,000!

Here are two recent works that relate to our story:

Seward, Desmond. *Napoleon's Family*, New York, Viking Penguin, 1986.

Wright, Constance. *Daughter to Napoleon. A Biography of Hortense, Queen of Holland*, Holt, Rinehart and Winston, New York, 1961.

C.B. Hase led a life *haute en couleurs*, as one editor put it. A good English language biography of Hase would make an amusing and lively addition to the Lives of the Scholars, which, for the most part – let's face it – are fairly drab. Readers who wish to delve a bit are referred to

von Hase, K.A. *Unsere Hauschronik. Geschichte der Familie Hase in vier Jahrhunderten*, Leipzig, 1898.

For critical judgments relating to Hase's alleged forgery, see

Sevcenko, Ihor. "The Date and Author of the So-Called Fragments of Toparcha Gothicus," *Dumbarton Oaks Papers* No. 25, Dumbarton Oaks, Washington, D.C., 1971, pp. 117–188.

This study also includes biographical information and conjectures as to the whereabouts of Hase's notorious *Secret Diary*.

For some mathematical details of Napoleon's Theorem and related ideas, see the bibliography to Chapter I of this book.

The quotation from W.H. Auden is from *Horae Canonicae*.

Chapter IV

Newspapers

The New York Times, November 27, 1986; March 22, 1990.

The Sunday Times (London), November 30, 1986; December 7, 1986.

The Independent (London), December 5, 1986.

The Christian Science Monitor (Boston), August 7, 1987.

The Times, London, May 16, 1990; May 18, 1990.

Books

Brendon, Piers. *Eminent Edwardians*, Houghton Mifflin, Boston (for Arthur Balfour).

Coraluppi, Georgio. *Factoring Large Integers*, Compumetrics, 1990.

Cornwell, David = Le Carré, John. See his spy novels.

Davis, P.J. *Spirals: From Theodorus to Chaos*, AK Peters, Wellesley, MA, 1993.

von Hapsburg, Rudolf. *Random Thoughts*, Vienna, State Archives.

Masters, Anthony. *Literary Agents: The Novelist as Spy*. Basil Blackwell, Oxford, 1987.

Pincher, Chapman. *Their Trade is Treachery*, London: Sidgwick and Jackson, 1981.

Rothschild, Emma. *Paradise Lost: The Decline of the Auto-Industrial Age*, New York: Random House, 1973.

Rothschild, Miriam. *Dear Lord Rothschild: Birds, Butterflies, and History*, Balaban, London, 1983.

Rothschild, Victor (3rd Baron Rothschild) [VR is often listed in library catalogues as Nathaniel Mayer Victor Rothschild]. A partial listing:

— *Fertilization*, New York: John Wiley, 1956.

— *Meditations of a Broomstick*, Collins, London, 1977.

— *The Rothschild Family Tree*, 1973; revised, 1981.

— *The Shadow of a Great Man*, published privately at New Court, St. Swithin's Lane, London, 1982.

— *Random Variables*, Collins, 1984.

Trevor-Roper, Hugh. *The Philby Affair*, London: Kimber, 1968.

West, Rebecca. *The Meaning of Treason*, London: Macmillan, 1949.

Wright, Peter. *Spy Catcher*, New York: Viking, 1987.

For Section 25

Ellison, William J. and Michel Mendes-France. *Les nombres premiers*, Hermann, Paris, 1975.

Kac, Mark. *Statistical Independence in Probability, Analysis and Number Theory*, Carus Mathematical Monograph No. 12, John Wiley, New York, 1959, pp. 74–79.

Riesel, Hans. *Prime Numbers and Computer Methods for Factorization*, Birkhäuser, Boston, 2nd ed., 1994.

Ribenboim, Paulo. *The Book of Prime Number Records*, Springer-Verlag, New York, 2nd ed., 1989. *The New Book of Prime Number Records*, to appear.

Shanks, Daniel, *Solved and Unsolved Problems in Number Theory*, Chelsea, 3rd ed., New York, 1985.

Philip J. Davis

Books by Philip J. Davis

Mathematical Monographs

Interpolation and Approximation

(with Philip Rabinowitz), *Methods of Numerical Integration*

Circulant Matrices

Spirals: From Theodorus to Chaos

Texts

The Mathematics of Matrices

Philosophy

(with Reuben Hersh), *The Mathematical Experience*

(with Reuben Hersh), *Descartes' Dream*

(with David Park), *No Way: The Nature of the Impossible*

Recreational

The Lore of Large Numbers

3.1416 and All That

Fiction (Possibly: Faction)

The Thread

Thomas Gray, Philosopher Cat

Thomas Gray in Copenhagen